Exploring *The* BUILDING BLOCKS *of* Science

Book 5

LABORATORY NOTEBOOK

REBECCA W. KELLER, PhD

Illustrations: Janet Moneymaker

Exploring the Building Blocks of Science Book 5 Laboratory Notebook
ISBN 978-1-941181-10-2

Published by Gravitas Publications Inc.
www.realscience4kids.com
www.gravitaspublications.com

Contents

Experiment 1

Writing History

Introduction

Explore your own history in this experiment.

I. Think About It

❶ Do you think you have a history? Why or why not?

_____

_____

_____

_____

_____

❷ Do you think knowing your history is important? Why or why not?

_____

_____

_____

_____

_____

❸ What history can you think of that was told to you by a parent?

_____

_____

_____

_____

_____

❹ Do you think any of your friends have ever told you some of their history? Why or why not?

_____

_____

_____

_____

❺ Do you think you could trace the history of your town all the way back to before the town was there? How would you do it?

_____

_____

_____

_____

❻ How do you think it could be helpful to know the history of how a technology was developed; for example, car engines or cell phones?

_____

_____

_____

_____

II. Experiment 1: Writing History   Date _____

Objective   To learn more about history by exploring my own history.

Hypothesis   By remembering events and using documents, I can record some of the history of my life.

Materials

photos, birth certificate, and other documents

EXPERIMENT

❶ Every person has a history. Write a short time line of your own history, starting when you were born and continuing up until today. Place at least four or five events on your time line. These might include events such as: My First Birthday, My Aunt's Wedding When I Was Two, etc.

History Time Line

Born _____

_____

_____

_____

_____

_____

_____

_____

_____

Today _____

❷ Think of some resources you might use to reconstruct your history in more detail and list them below. For example, you might use a birth certificate, photos, etc.

_____

_____

❸ Think about the histories of your grandfather and your grandmother. What resources could you use to reconstruct their histories?

_____

_____

❹ Think about your great-great-great-grandmother and your great-great-great-grandfather. What resources could you use to reconstruct their histories?

_____

_____

❺ Pick another member of your family whose history you can write. Gather the resources you will use to reconstruct their history and list them below.

_____

_____

_____

_____

_____

❻ Using the resources you collected, write a history of your family member.

History Time Line of _____

Born _____

_____

_____

_____

_____

_____

_____

_____

_____

_____

_____

_____

_____

_____

_____

_____

Today _____

_____

III. Conclusions

What conclusions about writing history can you draw from your observations?
Do you think it is easier to reconstruct your own history or the histories of
your great-great-great-grandparents? Why or why not?

_____

_____

_____

_____

_____

_____

_____

_____

_____

_____

_____

_____

_____

_____

_____

IV. Why?

It can be challenging to record an accurate history, even when it's the history of your own life. Documenting what happened, who said what, and when they said it is not always easy if it has been some time since the event occurred. Different people's memories of the same event may not be the same. Having photographs, diaries, newspaper clippings, home videos, and other documentation can be a big help in writing your history and that of your family.

In science, recording an accurate history is important if we want to understand both the successes and failures of the past and how to manage both resources and time in the future. Without a recorded history we don't know which experiments worked, which did not, and how to plan future work.

Scientists carefully record a history of each experiment they perform, including notes about what materials they used, what steps they followed, and what conclusions they drew from the results. By discovering which parts of an experiment work and which don't, scientists can understand how to make their experiments better and how to take the experiments in new directions to make new discoveries.

Also, when experimental processes and results are carefully recorded, scientists can share their research methods and findings with other scientists who can repeat these experiments to see if they get the same results. They can also expand on the information gained from the experimental histories to take the research in a different direction. It would be very difficult to make new discoveries if scientists did not have historical research records from which to draw knowledge and had to keep starting over or recreating experiments that had already been done.

V. Just For Fun

Think of one technological discovery that helped move science forward, for example, the microscope or the telescope. Do research online or at the library and write a brief history of the development of this technology.

A History of _____

_____

_____

_____

_____

_____

_____

_____

_____

_____

_____

_____

_____

_____

_____

_____

_____

_____

Experiment 2

Learning to Argue Scientifically

Introduction

In science, to "argue" means to present your point of view to someone who has an opposite or different point of view. An "argument" is the logic and data you used to arrive at a particular conclusion as well as a back and forth discussion. This experiment will help you learn how to argue like a scientist!

I. Think About It

❶ Think about a situation where you need to argue your side, or point of view, with a sibling or friend. Describe how you feel when you think about arguing your side. Do you feel calm or anxious? Do you feel excited or scared?

_____

_____

_____

_____

❷ Describe what happens in your body as you think about arguing your side. What do you think would help you stay calm as you argue your side?

_____

_____

_____

_____

CHEMISTRY

❸ Think about a situation where you need to argue your side with a parent, teacher, or another adult. Describe how you feel as you think about arguing your side. Do you feel calm or anxious? Do you feel excited or stressed?

_____

_____

_____

_____

_____

❹ Describe what happens in your body as you think about arguing your side with a parent, teacher, or another adult. What do you think would help you stay calm as you argue your side?

_____

_____

_____

_____

_____

❺ Is it easier to argue your side with a friend/sibling or with a parent/teacher or other adult? Why or why not?

_____

_____

_____

_____

_____

II. Experiment 2: Learning to Argue Scientifically—A Thought Experiment

Date _____

A thought experiment is done by thinking scientifically about how something might work without actually doing an experiment.

Objective To explore the importance of using scientific data to support scientific conclusions

Hypothesis By arguing with others about my ideas and using data to support my conclusions, I can learn about my own research and learn from others who may oppose my conclusions.

Materials

imagination

EXPERIMENT

❶ Read the following play.

The Mystery of Substance: A Philosophy Play
By D. R. Megill

ANAXIMANDER—believed everything is made up of "the boundless"

ANAXIMENES—believed everything is made up of air

THALES—believed everything is made up of water

DEMOCRITUS—believed everything is made up of atoms

Anaximander, Anaximenes, and Thales are having a heated argument. They are standing in a circle.

in the center of the city, Democritus is sitting on the ground building or playing with some sort of weird, unrecognizable materials [Legos]. It appears that Democritus is barely listening.

THALES: But it's obvious that everything comes from water! The very nature of life speaks to this. We could not live without water! Notice what happens when water is absent from a land for any period of time! It becomes barren, empty. Everything dies. Other forms of life come from water too: fish, frogs, and so on. Even our friend Democritus here on the ground (What are you doing, Dem?) must come from water.

ANAXIMANDER: But surely you see that there are things that could not possibly come from water. Things like earth and fire most certainly do not come from water.

THALES: Hmmm. Yes, fire presents a difficulty, considering that water destroys fire.

ANAXIMENES: I think you may have water on the brain, Thales. Rain drops from air. Thus, I am convinced by this, and by other proofs, that air is the source of all things! Air may take on different forms according to its different properties. In a rarefied form, it could even become fire. Fire can be destroyed not only by the addition of water, but more importantly, by the subtraction of air. This again, is proof of my point!

ANAXIMANDER: If Thales's head is full of water, does that mean yours is full of air, friend Anaximenes? I fear you are both wrong, but I don't fault you for it. It is very difficult to identify what things are made of.

THALES: You feel, no doubt, that you have done so?

ANAXIMANDER: Truth be told, yes, I have. It is hard to identify because we do not see it. We see only the parts into which it has been broken. Obviously, if it is the substance from which all things come, we cannot expect to see it in its initial form. We can, though, guess its nature from that which we do see. Tell me, what is true of everything?

ANAXIMENES: Everything has a purpose, I suppose.

THALES: *(looking down at Democritus on the ground)* Democritus here proves otherwise, Anaximenes. He serves no purpose at all, except to tinker with his strange objects.

CHEMISTRY

ANAXIMANDER: No, no, I will tell you what is true of all things. Everything has an opposite! Everything is equally balanced and measured by its opposite. If we could put all these things of opposite nature together, we would get a picture of a perfectly balanced, limitless substance. I call it, therefore, the boundless.

THALES: But what is the boundless, Nax?

ANAXIMANDER: I just told you. It is the thing from which all other things come.

ANAXIMENES: No, you just described it. What is it?

DEMOCRITUS: *(laughing in derision and without looking up)* You will never get the answer to that, my friends. He does not know! He is trying to befuddle you with fancy talk and imprecise terms. He speaks of a boundless, but it is only his imagination that is boundless, not his reasoning. You ask what all things are made of, and he answers that it is that from which all others come. Round and round it goes; where it stops, nobody knows.

ANAXIMANDER: I suppose you could do better then!

DEMOCRITUS: If you truly care to listen to the truth, you would be one of very few.

THALES: Well, I say we let him try, but for Zeus's sake, please stand up and look at us when you talk, as civil people do.

DEMOCRITUS: Well, I never claimed to be civil, but perhaps the argument will be a good break from my current exploration. (standing up) You are familiar, I hope, with the only reasonable man in Miletus, Leucippus.

ANAXIMANDER: Of course.

DEMOCRITUS: Well then, if you are familiar with Leucippus, perhaps this will sound familiar to you. I have only followed Leucippus's reasoning and observations to their obvious conclusion. There are two distinct problems. One is the problem of change, and the other is the problem of divisibility.

ANAXIMENES: What?

DEMOCRITUS: Things change. Haven't you noticed? How does a thing change from a basic substance into another thing? How can such a change be possible? As Empedocles of Elea has argued, change is rationally impossible, as it requires the existence of what is not.

ANAXIMANDER: And you accuse me of being obscure!

DEMOCRITUS: Let's leave the problem of change for now, and let's examine the other problem: divisibility. Imagine any element that you regard as the basic substance of things. It matters not what it is. Just imagine it. Now, divide it in half.

THALES: What? But what does that . . .

DEMOCRITUS: Can you do it? Can you picture dividing that substance in half?

THALES: Well, yes, of course, but . . .

DEMOCRITUS: Then that cannot be the basic substance. If it can be divided at all, it is not yet the basic substance. Rather, the two halves that you divided it into are the basic substances. Right?

THALES: Well, yes, you're right. But then, of course, that could be divided again.

DEMOCRITUS: Exactly! I am saying that, by definition, the most basic substance must be that which is no longer divisible.

ANAXIMENES: But no one has ever seen such a thing.

DEMOCRITUS: Of course no one has ever seen such a thing. Such a thing would be invisible to the naked eye. However, when combined with others of its kind, they would become visible. As you can see, the combinations by which these "indivisibles," or atoms, could combine would be virtually numberless, and by combining in different ways, they would make different things. This would explain the appearance of change by things that ultimately do not change.

THALES: Your ideas are nonsense, Democritus.

Democritus (begins laughing)

ANAXIMANDER: You are entertaining, Democritus, but obviously, going mad. It's clear by the way you go about laughing at everything all the time.

DEMOCRITUS: If you could see how ridiculous you all are, you and all the others, you would laugh too.

ANAXIMENES: I fear my friends are right. You are clearly either crazy or stupid. These toys of yours, Democritus, what are they?

DEMOCRITUS: I knew you would not listen. Now, if you don't mind, I'd like to get back to my current exploration. *(Democritus kneels back down on the ground.)* If you must know, my nephew invented these. They are a good example of my atomic ideas. These little pieces can be rearranged into various shapes and can be used over and over without any seeming decay. My nephew has named them after his father, my brother, Legosus.

THALES: You have to admit, guys, that water is almost as indivisible as Democritus. I told you I was right.

Anaximander, Anaximenes, and Thales begin walking away from Democritus.

ANAXIMENES: *(to Thales)* You are as crazy as he is.

ANAXIMANDER: I'm telling you, it's the boundless. Let me show you.

(END)

❷ According to Democritus, what is the primary substance? Explain his description.

_____

_____

_____

_____

_____

_____

CHEMISTRY

CHEMISTRY

❸ Do the other philosophers believe Democritus? Why or why not?

_____

_____

_____

_____

_____

_____

❹ List some points made by each of the philosophers.

ANAXIMANDER _____

_____

ANAXIMENES _____

_____

THALES _____

_____

DEMOCRITUS _____

_____

Results

❶ If you lived in ancient Greece and didn't know what we now know about matter, which of the philosophers' arguments would you have found most convincing? What points did he make that convinced you?

_____

_____

_____

_____

_____

_____

❷ Imagine that you are a young Einstein working as a clerk in a patent office. You come up with a radical new idea for how light and matter interact. This idea goes against the standard scientific theories of the day and is opposed by many established scientists. How would you argue for your discovery?

_____

_____

_____

_____

_____

_____

_____

CHEMISTRY

III. Conclusions

What conclusions about arguing scientifically can you draw from your observations?

_____

_____

_____

_____

_____

_____

_____

_____

_____

_____

_____

_____

_____

_____

_____

_____

_____

CHEMISTRY

IV. Why?

By doing thought experiments, you can get an idea for how an experiment or argument may go without having actual data. Thought experiments are useful because they can prepare us for real experiments or help us develop ideas about an experiment that is impossible to perform.

In this thought experiment you read a short fictional play about how an argument between philosophers with opposing viewpoints may have transpired. In the play you saw how the philosophers had different theories about what the world is made of, and each brought up different points to back up his own theory. You saw how they had a back and forth discussion that was sometimes heated.

You may have noticed that the framework you learned from the play helped you form the hypothetical argument for a new theory about how light and matter interact. Practicing thought experiments can help you frame your own arguments and can help you become clearer about your ideas and how to express them to others in an understandable way.

Scientists use thought experiments as a way of thinking deeply about ideas. If their ideas lead to an actual experiment, they think about what the experiment might be expected to show or prove, how a physical experiment might be set up, what steps must be followed in performing the experiment, and what outcomes might occur. It is important in planning an experiment to think about as many factors involved as possible before beginning. When the experiment has been completed, the scientists will review the results to see if the expected outcome happened or if something else occurred. They might ask what would happen if some part of the experiment were changed. Would they get a different result? If they get unexpected results, they might look back at the experiment to see if all the steps were performed correctly, or they might realize they have made a new discovery.

V. Just For Fun

Imagine you are on a strange new planet. It has elements, just like planet Earth, and you discover everything seems to be made of candy.

List the experiments you might perform to prove or disprove your hypothesis that everything is made of candy.

Testing a Candy Planet

_____

_____

_____

_____

_____

_____

_____

_____

_____

_____

_____

_____

CHEMISTRY

What Is It Made Of?

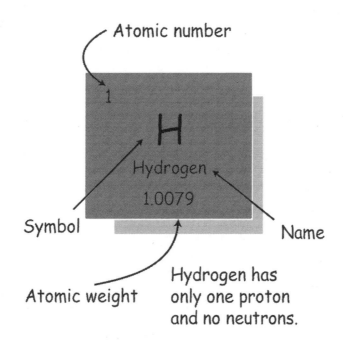

Atomic number

1

H

Hydrogen

1.0079

Symbol

Name

Atomic weight

Hydrogen has only one proton and no neutrons.

CHEMISTRY

Introduction

Discover what things are made of!

I. Think About It

❶ Do you think all atoms are the same? Why or why not?

_____

_____

_____

_____

_____

❷ If you wanted to find out how much an atom weighs, how would you do it?

_____

_____

_____

_____

_____

❸ What things do you think you could find out about atoms by looking at a periodic table of elements?

_____

_____

_____

_____

_____

CHEMISTRY

❹ What do you think your favorite breakfast food is made of?

_____

_____

_____

_____

❺ If you wanted to know the details of what your favorite breakfast food is made of, how would you find out?

_____

_____

_____

_____

❻ Do you think it's important to know what things are made of? Why or why not?

_____

_____

_____

_____

II. Experiment 3: What Is It Made Of?   Date _____

CHEMISTRY

Objective   To become familiar with the periodic table of elements and investigate the composition of some common items

Hypothesis _____

_____

_____

Materials

food labels
periodic table of elements from *Student Textbook*
resources (books or online) such as:
  dictionary
  encyclopedia
computer with internet access (optional)

EXPERIMENT

❶ Using the periodic table of elements, answer the following questions:

A. How many protons does aluminum have?   _____

How many electrons?   _____

B. What is the symbol for carbon?   _____

C. List all the elements that have chemical properties similar to helium.

_____

_____

_____

D. What is the atomic weight of nitrogen?   _____

How many neutrons does nitrogen have?   _____

❷ In the table on the next page, fill in the following information:

▶ **ITEM**

Think of several different items and write them in the column labeled ITEM. These can be any item, like "tires" or "cereal." Try to be specific. For example, instead of writing just "cereal," write "corn cereal" or "sweet, colored cereal."

▶ **COMPOSITION**

In an encyclopedia, on the food label, or online, look up the composition of the items you have selected, and write this information in the column labeled COMPOSITION. Try to be as specific as possible when identifying the composition. For example, if your cereal contains vitamin C, write "sodium ascorbate" if that name is also listed. Try to identify any elements that are in the compounds you have listed. For example, vitamin C contains the element "sodium."

▶ **SOURCE**

Write the source in the column next to the composition. "Source" means where you got your information; for example, "food label" or "encyclopedia," or if you got the information online, list the name of the website.

CHEMISTRY

ITEM	COMPOSITION	SOURCE

Results

Briefly describe what you discovered about the composition of the various items.

For example:

Kellogg's Sugar Smacks cereal contains vitamin C, which is called

sodium ascorbate.

_____

_____

_____

_____

_____

_____

_____

_____

_____

_____

_____

_____

III. Conclusions

State your conclusions based on the information you collected.

For example:

Many cereals contain sodium in the form of salt and vitamin C.

_____

_____

_____

_____

_____

_____

_____

_____

_____

_____

_____

_____

_____

_____

CHEMISTRY

IV. Why?

In order to do chemistry, scientists need to know the properties of atoms. The properties of all the atoms, or elements, that make up all living and nonliving things are in the periodic table of elements. The periodic table is a large chart that organizes and categorizes all of the elements according to their chemical properties and shows the underlying order that exists among the elements.

The periodic table gets its name because it shows the general law of *periodicity* among all of the elements. This means that certain chemical properties of the atoms repeat. Grouping the elements according to their chemical properties gives rise to the "periods" which are the horizontal rows. These rows are organized by the number of protons an element contains, starting with hydrogen which has one proton. As you go across the row, the elements have increasingly larger numbers of protons. The last naturally occurring element is uranium with 92 protons. The elements after uranium are artificially made.

The columns in the periodic table organize the elements by their chemical properties. For example, fluorine (F) undergoes chemical reactions similar to those of chlorine (Cl), bromine (Br), iodine (I), and astatine (At). All of these similar elements are arranged in a single column of the periodic table.

The symbols for different atoms can be used in writing about them so the whole name doesn't need to be written out. Because the periodic table lists the symbols for all the elements, all scientists will know what a certain symbol means when they are looking at someone else's work.

Knowing the properties of the different types of atoms helps scientists understand how the atoms will or won't combine with each other. Also, when chemists are measuring amounts of the different substances needed for a chemical reaction, knowing the atomic weights of the different atoms can help them measure out the proper amounts.

V. Just For Fun

Select one or more items from your chart. Find out as much as you can about how it was made, where it was made, and where the different components it is made of might have come from.

CHEMISTRY

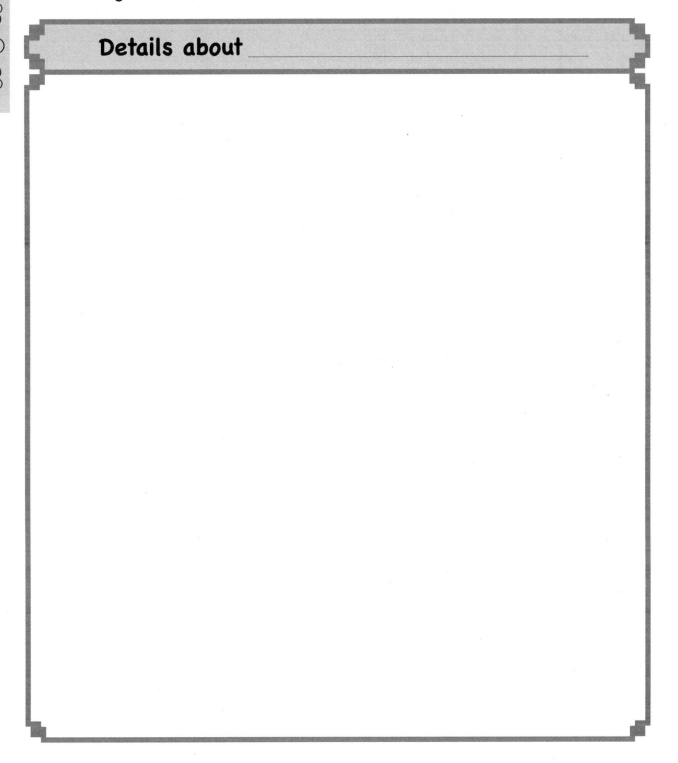

Details about _____

Modeling Molecules

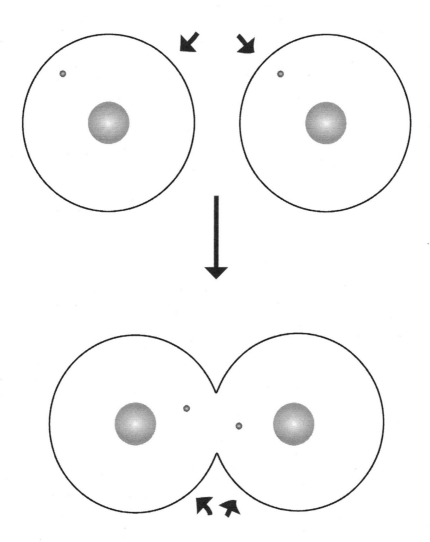

Introduction

Build models to explore how atoms combine to make molecules.

I. Think About It

CHEMISTRY

❶ What are some rules you follow?

_____

_____

_____

_____

_____

❷ What do you think life would be like if there were no rules?

_____

_____

_____

_____

_____

❸ Do you think atoms can join to make molecules without following any rules? Why or why not?

_____

_____

_____

_____

_____

❹ Do you think all atoms follow exactly the same rules when making molecules? Why or why not?

_____

_____

_____

_____

❺ What do you think life on Earth would be like if atoms did not combine to form molecules?

_____

_____

_____

_____

❻ What do you think life on Earth would be like if atoms did not follow rules to make molecules but could combine in any way?

_____

_____

_____

_____

CHEMISTRY

II. Experiment 4: Modeling Molecules   Date _____

Objective   To make models of molecules from marshmallows and toothpicks
to show how atoms fit together

Hypothesis _____

_____

_____

CHEMISTRY

Materials

small, colored marshmallows
large marshmallows
toothpicks

EXPERIMENT

❶ Take several marshmallows of both sizes and several toothpicks.

❷ Make shapes from the marshmallows and toothpicks. First, form any number
of links between marshmallows (put any number of toothpicks into each
marshmallow). Draw the shapes below, noting the number of toothpicks in
each marshmallow.

❸ Using new marshmallows, assign an "atom" to each of the marshmallows. The large marshmallows should be C, N, and O, and the small marshmallows should be H and Cl. Use the following "rules" for the number of toothpicks that can go into a marshmallow.

C (carbon) – 4 toothpicks all pointing away from each other

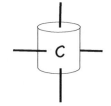

N (nitrogen) – 3 toothpicks pointing downward

O (oxygen) – 2 toothpicks pointing downward

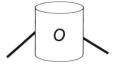

H (hydrogen) and **Cl** (chlorine) – 1 toothpick pointing in any direction

Cl or H

Results

❶ Make the following molecules from your marshmallow atoms.

To make each molecule, follow the rules in Step ❸. In the following chart, draw the shape of each molecule you make.

H₂O   This is one oxygen and two hydrogens. (water)

NH₃   This is one nitrogen and three hydrogens. (ammonia)

CH₄   This is one carbon and four hydrogens. (methane)

CH₃OH   This is one carbon with three hydrogens and one oxygen attached. The oxygen has one hydrogen attached to it. (methanol)

CHEMISTRY

H_2O	NH_3
CH_4	CH_3OH

III. Conclusions

What conclusions can you draw from your observations?

_____

_____

_____

_____

_____

_____

_____

_____

_____

_____

_____

_____

_____

_____

_____

CHEMISTRY

IV. Why?

In this experiment you explored one method of modeling molecules. In the molecule models you built, the marshmallows represent the atoms and the toothpicks represent the bonds between the atoms. Each toothpick also represents the electrons that are available for bonding, with one electron at each end of the toothpick.

The maximum number of bonds an atom can form depends on the number of available electrons. To form a bond, two electrons are required, one from each atom. The electron that forms a bond must be available, and most atoms have additional electrons that are not available for bonding.

Atoms follow rules to form bonds with other atoms.

By doing this experiment you saw how there are fewer possible molecules that can form when atoms follow rules than there would be if atoms did not follow rules. "Fewer possible molecules" means that the molecules that make up the world have specific rather than random structures. If atoms did not follow rules, there would be no telling what the result would be when atoms joined together—it would be entirely unpredictable!

Each kind of atom has its own special properties; therefore, when atoms are combined, the result is molecules with special properties. Since molecules have special properties, higher structures, such as tissues, plants, stars, jellyfish, and pudding, also have special properties.

When two or more atoms combine, the resulting molecules have particular shapes. The shapes depend on the number of electrons in each atom and the type of bond they form. Right now, it is not important to know the details of how molecules are shaped. The thing to remember is:

The shapes of molecules obey rules.

V. Just For Fun

Following the rules outlined in Step ❸ for the marshmallow molecules, make different "molecules." Make as many different shapes as you can without breaking the rules. Draw your shapes below and write down how many of each kind of atom and how many bonds are in each molecule.

Identifying Chemical Reactions

Introduction

See if you can observe chemical reactions taking place.

I. Think About It

❶ Do you think chemical reactions happen every day? Why or why not?

_____

_____

_____

_____

_____

❷ Do you think you can tell whether or not a chemical reaction has taken place? How could you tell?

_____

_____

_____

_____

_____

❸ Do you think chemical reactions happen with foods? Why or why not?

_____

_____

_____

_____

_____

CHEMISTRY

CHEMISTRY

❹ If two substances are mixed together and have a chemical reaction, will there always be a chemical reaction when those substances are mixed? Why or why not?

_____

_____

_____

_____

❺ What are some chemical reactions you think you have observed?

_____

_____

_____

_____

❻ If there were no chemical reactions, do you think life could exist? Why or why not?

_____

_____

_____

_____

II. Experiment 5: Identifying Chemical Reactions

Date _____

Objective   In this experiment we will try to identify a chemical reaction by observing the changes that occur when two solutions are added together.

Hypothesis   A chemical reaction can be identified by observing changes that occur in the course of the reaction.

Materials

    baking soda
    lemon juice
    balsamic vinegar
    salt and water:
        15-30 ml salt dissolved in 120 ml water
        (1-2 tbsp. salt dissolved in 1/2 cup of water)
    egg whites
    milk
    7 small jars
    measuring cups and spoons
    eye dropper

EXPERIMENT

❶ Put a small amount of each of the substances listed into its own jar. Examine the contents of each jar, taking note of the properties of each substance. Record the color, texture, and odor next to each item on the materials list. Don't taste the substances.

❷ Using the chart in the *Results* section, write down all of the substances (baking soda, lemon juice, balsamic vinegar, saltwater, egg whites, and milk) horizontally with one item above each column.

Write the same list of items vertically down the left side of the grid next to each row. There should be an item assigned to each column and to each row.

❸ In the white boxes in the following chart record what you observe when a small amount of the item listed in the column is mixed with a small amount the item in the corresponding row. Use a separate jar for mixing and rinse it out in between tests, or use more jars. Look especially for changes that indicate a chemical reaction has taken place. For example, look for bubbles, color change, or a precipitate.

Results

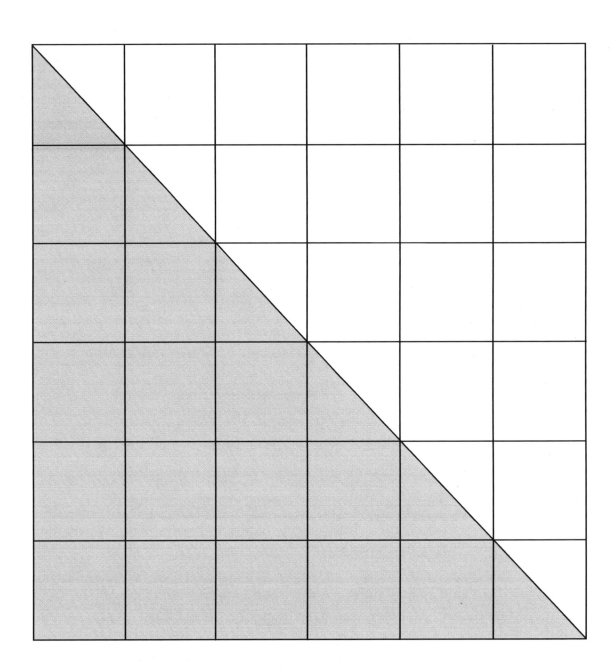

Results for Unknown Solutions

❶ Ask your teacher for two unknown solutions. Describe their properties.

Describe each unknown solution.

A _____

_____

B _____

_____

❷ Mix them. Describe the results and why you think a chemical reaction did or did not take place.

Results of the two unknowns being mixed:

_____

_____

_____

_____

❸ Record your ideas about what the unknown substances are and what observations you used to identify them.

A _____

_____

B _____

_____

III. Conclusions

What conclusions can you draw from your observations?

_____

_____

_____

_____

_____

_____

_____

_____

_____

_____

_____

_____

_____

_____

_____

_____

_____

_____

CHEMISTRY

IV. Why?

Chemical reactions occur everywhere. For example:

- Stomach acid reacts with food to help us digest it.
- Cars are powered by the combustion (chemical reaction) of gasoline with oxygen from the air.
- When iron is left outside it reacts with oxygen and rust forms.
- When hair is straightened or permed, sulfur bonds are broken and reformed.

In this chapter of the *Student Textbook* you learned about four main types of chemical reactions—combination reactions, decomposition reactions, displacement reactions, and exchange reactions. Most chemical reactions fall into these categories or are combinations of these categories.

There are several indicators that tell scientists when a chemical reaction has taken place. These include bubbles, color change, heat exchange, and precipitation. Sometimes more than one of these indicators can occur at the same time. For example, both bubbles and heat can be given off together. Sometimes none of them occur, and more subtle methods must be used to detect the reaction.

Bubbles form when one of the molecules produced is a gas. Color changes may indicate that a particular element is a substance involved in the chemical reaction. A solution might either give off heat *(exothermic reaction)* or take in heat *(endothermic reaction)*. Precipitations occur when one or more products of the reaction can no longer be dissolved in the solution.

Much of the time scientists are trying to figure out how to identify unknowns. In this experiment you observed all of the reactants both before and after a reaction. This gave you the knowledge to be able to identify an unknown. By knowing about the properties of different elements and the different types of chemical reactions, scientists are better able to identify unknowns.

V. Just For Fun

Watch baking soda decompose (undergo a decomposition reaction) and give off carbon dioxide gas while peanut brittle is being made.

Peanut Brittle

360 ml (1 1/2 cups) sugar
240 ml (1 cup) white corn syrup
120 ml (1/2 cup) water
360 ml (1 1/2 cups) raw peanuts (can be omitted)
5 ml (1 teaspoon) baking soda
buttered pan

Boil sugar, water, and syrup in a sauce pan over medium heat until the mixture turns a little brown. Add 360 ml (1 1/2 cups) raw peanuts Stir until golden brown. Don't over-brown. Add 5 ml (1 teaspoon) baking soda. Spread on buttered pan.

What evidence did you see of a chemical reaction occurring while you were making peanut brittle? What other evidence of chemical reactions have you observed while food items are being cooked or after they have been cooked? Record your observations on the following page

Evidence of Chemical Reactions in Food

Experiment 6

Putting Things in Order

Introduction

Explore sorting objects by putting them in categories.

I. Think About It

❶ What are some groups, or categories, of foods that you can think of?

_____

_____

_____

_____

❷ What are some groups, or categories, of toys that you can think of?

_____

_____

_____

_____

❸ In what other ways could you group foods or toys?

_____

_____

_____

_____

BIOLOGY

❹ Do you think it is helpful to you to put objects into different groups? Why or why not?

_____

_____

_____

_____

❺ In what ways might it be helpful for scientists to put objects into different groups?

_____

_____

_____

_____

❻ What do you think would happen if biologists tried to study each living thing by itself instead of placing it in a group?

_____

_____

_____

_____

II. Experiment 6: Putting Things in Order   Date _____

Objective   _____

_____

Hypothesis   _____

_____

_____

Materials

pencil and eraser

Collect a variety of objects. Some suggestions are:

rubber ball
cotton ball
orange
banana
apple
paper
sticks
leaves
rocks
grass
Legos
building blocks
other objects

EXPERIMENT

❶ Spread all the objects out on a table. Carefully look at each object and note some of its characteristics. For example, some objects may be smooth, some fuzzy; some may be edible, others not; some may be large, some small, etc.

❷ In the following chart, record your observations for each item.

Item	Characteristics

BIOLOGY

❸ Now try to define "categories" for the objects. For example, some objects may be "hard," so one category could be called "Hard." Some objects may be "round," so another category could be "Round." Try to think of at least 4 or 5 different categories for your objects. Write the categories along the top of the following table.

❹ List the objects in the category that describes them. Take note of those objects that fit into more than one category. Write these objects down more than once, placing them in all of the categories that describe them.

❺ Next, take a look at each of the categories and each of the objects in those categories. Can you make "subcategories?" For example, some objects may all be the same color, so "Red" could be a subcategory. Some may be food items so "Food" could be a subcategory. Pick three categories and try to list two subcategories for each of these main categories.

❻ List the objects according to their category and subcategory. See if you can fit all the objects into a category and subcategory. You can rename your categories and subcategories as needed.

BIOLOGY

Categories						

BIOLOGY

Categories					
Sub-categories					

III. Conclusions

What conclusions can you draw from your observations?

_____

_____

_____

_____

_____

_____

_____

_____

_____

_____

_____

_____

_____

_____

BIOLOGY

IV. Why?

As you discovered in this experiment, it can be difficult to sort objects into exact groups because the objects have so many different features. Some of the objects you looked at could fit into two or more groups depending on their features and the way you defined the groups. It can take some time to figure out how to define groups in order to accommodate all the items being categorized. Once the main categories have been determined, objects that all fit into one of the main categories can then be placed into smaller subcategories according to additional features.

The same is true when scientists are putting living things into groups. There are so many different types of living things with so many different characteristics that it can be difficult to determine which organisms should be grouped together. When classifying living things, scientists first divide them into several very large groups. In the classification system used in this chapter of the *Student Textbook,* organisms are first grouped into domains according to the type of cell they are made of. Then each domain is divided into one or more kingdoms, then kingdoms into phyla. Each group is further divided until the level of genus and species is reached, which defines the particular type of organism. As you can see, taxonomic classification starts out with groups that contain very large numbers of organisms, and the number of organisms in a group gets smaller as more characteristics are considered.

These taxonomic categories can change or become outdated. New classification systems are developed as scientists make new discoveries and as they need to categorize organisms in ways that are more suited to what is being studied.

V. Just For Fun

On the next page write down the names of 15 or more living things you can see without a microscope or magnifying glass.

Make up your own taxonomic system. Put the living things you've written down into main categories and then as many sub-categories as you can according to their different features. Give your taxonomic system a name and name your categories and sub-categories. Record your taxonomic chart on the following page. Use additional paper if needed.

Living things: _____

_____

_____

_____

_____

What's in Spit?

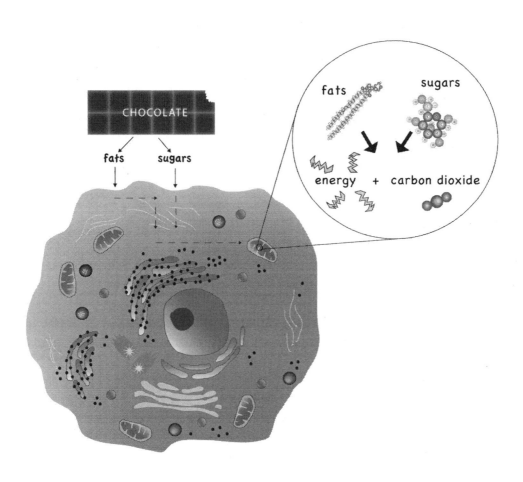

Introduction

Discover what happens to bread when it's in your mouth.

I. Think About It

❶ What do you think happens when you chew food?

_____

_____

_____

_____

❷ What do you think the saliva in your mouth does?

_____

_____

_____

_____

❸ Do you think you could eat bread if you did not have saliva? Why or why not?

_____

_____

_____

_____

BIOLOGY

❹ Do you think all digestion of food happens in the stomach? Why or why not?

_____

_____

_____

_____

_____

❺ Do you think there are any differences in how your body digests bread and how it digests celery?

_____

_____

_____

_____

_____

❻ Do you think saliva is part of a metabolic process? Why or why not?

_____

_____

_____

_____

_____

II. Experiment 7: What's in Spit?   Date _____

Objective _____

_____

Hypothesis _____

_____

_____

Materials

tincture of iodine [**VERY POISONOUS—DO NOT EAT** any food items that
  have iodine on them]
bread
timer
wax paper
marking pen
cup

EXPERIMENT

❶ Break the bread into several small pieces.

❷ Chew one piece for 30 seconds (use the timer), chew another piece for
   1 minute, and a third piece for as long as possible (several minutes).

❸ Each time, after chewing the bread, spit it onto a piece of wax paper. Using
   the marking pen, label the wax paper with the length of time the bread
   has been chewed.

❹ Take three small pieces of unchewed bread, and place one next to each of
   the chewed pieces.

❺ Add a drop of iodine to each piece of bread—chewed and unchewed.

❻ Record your observations in the following chart.

Chewed Bread			
30 Seconds	**1 Minute**	**Several Minutes**	**Unchewed Bread**

❼ Take two more pieces of bread. Collect as much saliva from your mouth as you can (spit into a cup several times). Soak both pieces of bread in the saliva.

❽ Place each piece of soaked bread on a piece of wax paper. Put one piece in the refrigerator and leave the other one at room temperature. Let them sit for 30 minutes.

❾ After 30 minutes add a drop of iodine to each.

❿ Record your results.

Bread + Saliva — 30 Minutes	
Refrigerated	**Not Refrigerated**

III. Conclusions

What conclusions can you draw from your observations?

_____

_____

_____

_____

_____

_____

_____

_____

_____

_____

_____

_____

_____

_____

_____

BIOLOGY

BIOLOGY

IV. Why?

In this experiment you saw how your saliva begins the process of food being digested.

Your body gets much of its energy from *starches* in foods. Starches are long chains of sugar molecules that have to be broken down into single sugar molecules called glucose before the sugars can be used by your body for energy. *Amylose* is a starch that is found in foods such as bread and potatoes.

Amylase is a protein called an *enzyme,* and it is found in saliva. Amylase is a molecular machine that cuts a long chain of amylose into individual sugar molecules. When we chew food, the amylase protein begins to digest (break down) amylose starch molecules in our mouth before we even swallow. Our bodies can then use these sugar molecules for energy.

In this experiment iodine reacts with starch and turns black. Iodine doesn't react with glucose. Therefore, the more the bread was chewed and the more the starch was broken down into glucose by the amylase, the less of a color change you saw with the iodine.

The names of amylose and amylase are very similar. Many enzymes (protein machines) are named after the molecules they work on. An enzyme is a protein molecular machine that carries out different functions, such as breaking down food molecules. Amylase is the enzyme that breaks down amylose, the starch. Notice that the endings differ: "-ase" for the enzyme, "-ose" for the starch.

Enzymes are highly specific. That is, each type of enzyme works only on a certain type of molecule. Amylase does not digest cellulose, only amylose. Cellulase, a different enzyme, digests cellulose. The name of an enzyme usually tells which molecule the enzyme works on.

Scientists still do not know everything about all of the proteins inside cells and the roles they play. Many proteins are very complex. Protein machines act as very sophisticated motors, rotors, gears, pumps, and scissors. We have not yet learned to build machinery that has the precision and complexity of these remarkable molecular machines.

V. Just For Fun

Repeat the experiment using celery, kale, or another green vegetable. You can also test other vegetables or fruits of your choice. Compare your results to what you found with bread. What conclusions can you draw?

Chewed Vegetables			
30 Seconds	**1 Minute**	**Several Minutes**	**Unchewed**

Vegetable + Saliva — 30 Minutes	
Refrigerated	**Not Refrigerated**

BIOLOGY

Experiment 8

Inside the Cell

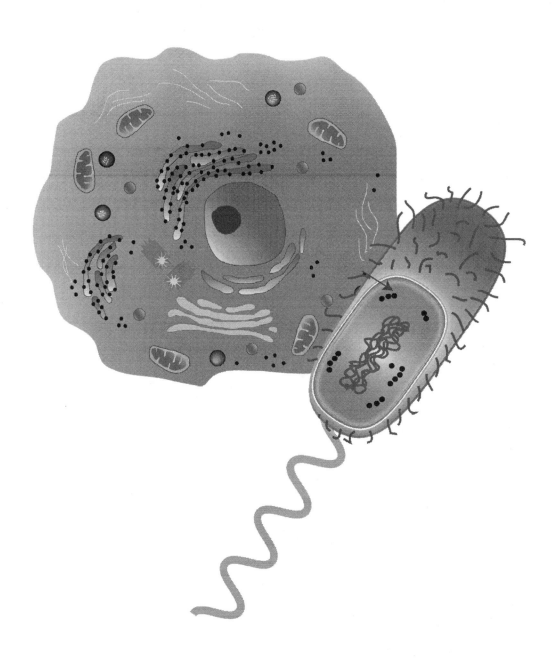

Introduction

Learn more about different types of cells by comparing their features.

I. Think About It

❶ Can you think of any living things that are not made of cells? Why or why not?

_____

_____

_____

_____

❷ Do you think all the cells in an animal are exactly alike? Why or why not?

_____

_____

_____

_____

❸ Do you think all cells perform most of the same functions as each other in order to live? Why or why not?

_____

_____

_____

_____

_____

BIOLOGY

❹ Do you think it is possible to look at one cell and tell whether it comes from a plant or a bacterium? Why or why not?

_____

_____

_____

_____

❺ Do you think an animal could have a prokaryotic cell? Why or why not?

_____

_____

_____

_____

❻ Do you think knowing about cells helps scientists learn about living things? Why or why not?

_____

_____

_____

_____

BIOLOGY

II. Experiment 8: Inside the Cell   Date _____

Objective Comparing the drawings of the bacterial prokaryotic cell, the plant cell, and the animal cell in the *Student Textbook,* we will observe which features are similar and which are different.

Materials

pencil
colored pencils or crayons

EXPERIMENT

List some things you observe in the drawings in the textbook that are similar for all three cell types:

_____

_____

_____

List some observations of things that are different:

_____

_____

_____

List the function of each of the following:

nucleus _____

mitochondria _____

chloroplasts _____

cell wall _____

lysosome _____

peroxisome _____

❶ Animal cells differ from plant cells, and both plant and animal cells differ from bacterial cells.

List as many differences as you can between plants, animals, and bacteria, and explain why you think their cells may need to be different.

Bacteria have or don't have	Plants have or don't have	Animals have or don't have

BIOLOGY

_____

_____

_____

_____

❷ Without looking at your textbook, fill in the blanks with as many names for the structures in the cell as you can.

Is this an animal cell, a plant cell, or a bacterial prokaryotic cell? Write the cell type at the top. Color the cell.

_____

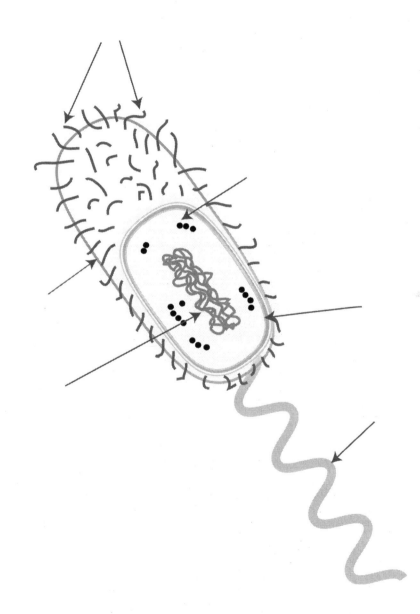

❸ Without looking at your textbook, fill in the blanks with as many names for the structures in the cell as you can.

Is this an animal cell, a plant cell, or a bacterial prokaryotic cell? Write the cell type at the top. Color the cell.

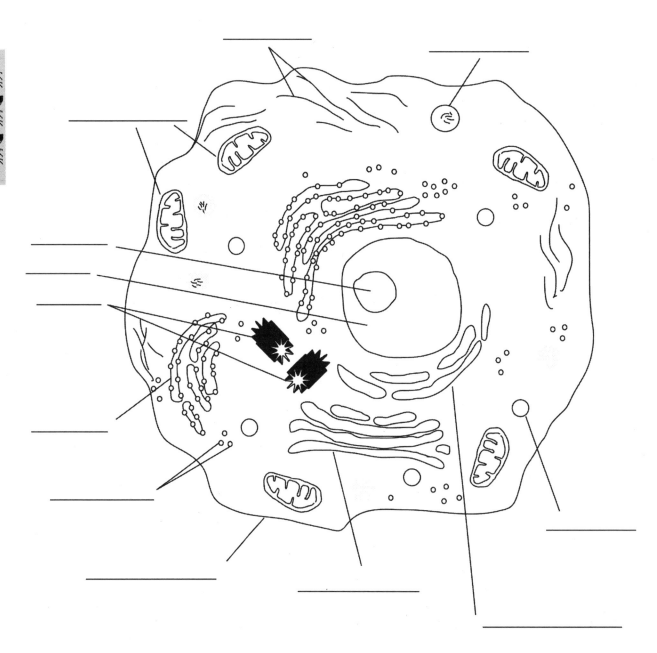

❹   Without looking at your textbook, fill in the blanks with as many names for the structures in the cell as you can.

Is this an animal cell, a plant cell, or a bacterial prokaryotic cell? Write the cell type at the top. Color the cell.

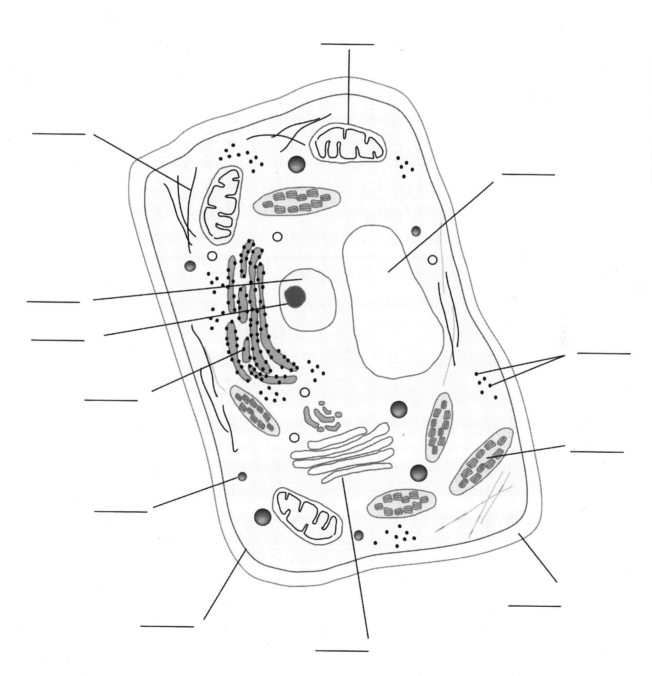

III. Conclusions

What conclusions can you draw about cells from your observations?

BIOLOGY

IV. Why?

All living things are made of cells. There are no living things that are not made of cells. We know a lot about what cells look like, what they contain, and how they work. However, we are still very far from understanding everything about cells. Even the simplest cells are incredibly complex.

In this experiment we looked at bacterial prokaryotic cells, animal cells, and plant cells. Animals and plants have eukaryotic cells. Eukaryotic cells have organelles, and bacterial prokaryotic cells do not have organelles. This does not mean that prokaryotic cells are not complex, only that they do not have the same features as eukaryotic cells.

The cell drawings in this experiment represent a generalized cell. For animals and plants, there are many different kinds of cells. Animals can have bone cells, nerve cells, and skin cells, all with slightly different features. Plants can have root cells, leaf cells, and seed cells. All of these cells are eukaryotic cells, but each is specialized to perform a particular task for the animal or plant.

Prokaryotes are considered simple cells because they lack many features that eukaryotes possess. For example, prokaryotes do not have a membrane-bound nucleus, while eukaryotes do. Many prokaryotic cells have flagella or pili that move the organism. A prokaryotic cell may also use pili to attach itself to surfaces and to other cells.

Plants are made of eukaryotic cells. Plant cells have both a membrane-bound nucleus and organelles. Plant cells have a cell wall that gives plants the stiffness they need for standing upright. Plants also have chloroplasts. Chloroplasts are organelles that are used by the cell to make food by photosynthesis. These two features, cell walls and chloroplasts, make plant cells different from animal cells.

Animal cells have many of the same organelles as plant cells. Both plant and animal cells have mitochondria, a nucleus, and ribosomes. Animal cells differ from plant cells in several important ways. First, animal cells do not have chloroplasts and do not use the Sun's energy to make food. Animal cells also do not have cell walls, and they lack the central vacuole found in plant cells. So, although plant and animal cells have many similar features and are both eukaryotes, plant and animal cells are also different.

V. Just For Fun

Choose one of the cells from this experiment and make a model of it. Use your labeled drawing as a plan for building the model. Before beginning your model, think about what materials you could use for different features, and in the following box make a list of materials to choose from. Then build your model!

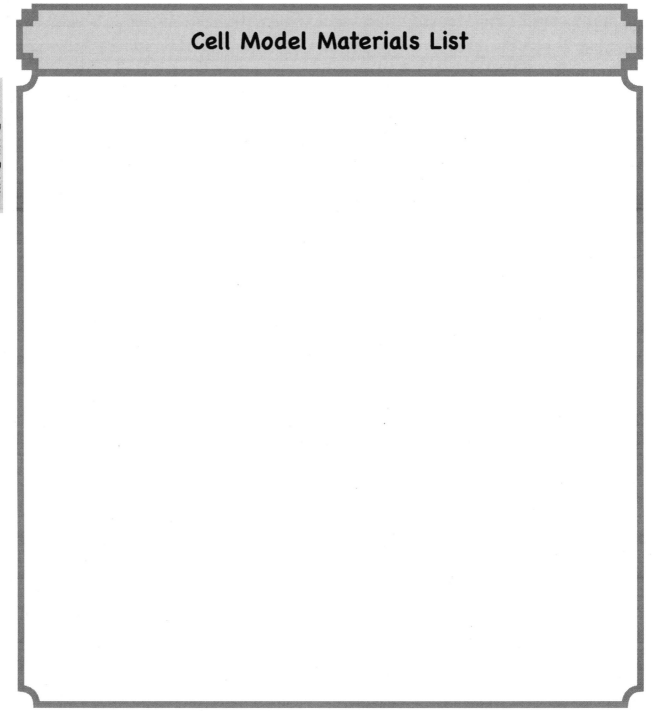

Cell Model Materials List

Experiment 9

Wash Your Hands!

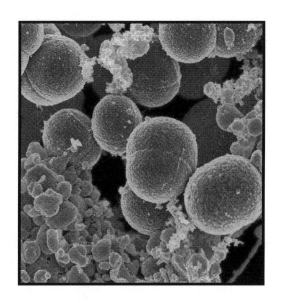

Introduction

Do you think you can find bacteria?

I. Think About It

1 If you were to find bacteria, where do you think it would be? Why?

_____

_____

_____

_____

2 Why do you need to wash your hands after being outside?

_____

_____

_____

_____

3 Why do you need to wash your hands after using the bathroom?

_____

_____

_____

_____

❹ Do you think your hands are "clean" after you wash them? Why or why not?

_____

_____

_____

_____

_____

❺ Do you think the surfaces in your house, like the computer terminal and kitchen door knob are clean? Why are why not?

_____

_____

_____

_____

_____

BIOLOGY

❻ Do you think bacteria can be good for you, bad for you, both, or neither? Why?

_____

_____

_____

_____

_____

II. Experiment 9: Wash Your Hands!   Date _____

Objective _____

_____

Hypothesis _____

_____

_____

BIOLOGY

Materials

    dehydrated agar powder
    distilled water
    cooking pot
    measuring spoons
    measuring cup
    cup
    plastic petri dishes
    cotton swabs
    permanent marker
    oven mitt or pot holder

EXPERIMENT

In this experiment you will be culturing bacteria—growing bacteria in a specially prepared substance that contains nutrients needed for growth. For the bacteria to grow, it also needs to be incubated, or kept under conditions that are favorable for growth. The petri dishes prepared with agar are called plates.

Part I: Preparing Agar Plates

❶ Being careful not to remove the lids, spread the petri dishes on a clean counter top.

❷ Add 10 ml (2 teaspoons) dehydrated agar powder to 200 ml (about 1 cup) room temperature distilled water. Bring to a boil while stirring.

❸ Using an oven mitt or pot holder, hold in one hand the cooking pot containing the hot agar. With the other hand gently slide the petri dish lid to the side and pour in enough hot agar to just cover the bottom. Carefully slide the petri dish lid back on to cover the agar. Repeat for all petri dishes.

❹ Allow the agar in the petri dish to cool completely. It will form a hard surface.

❺ Once cooled, gently turn the petri dishes over while keeping the lids on, and stack them. Turning the petri dishes upside down prevents condensation from collecting on the agar.

❻ Store them in the refrigerator until you are ready to use them.

Part II: Testing for Bacteria

❶ Remove one petri dish from the refrigerator and label it "Agar." Return it to the refrigerator until it is time for incubation.

❷ Remove a second petri dish and label it "Water."

❸ Take a clean cotton swab and swirl it in a cup of distilled water. Shake the swab to remove excess water. Take the wet swab and "streak" the agar side of the petri dish labeled "Water." To streak the agar plate, start at one edge of the agar and move the swab toward the opposite side of the petri dish with a zigzag motion. Be careful not to push too hard so you don't break the surface of the agar.

❹ Remove a third agar plate from the refrigerator and label it "Hands."

❺ Take a clean cotton swab, swirl it in a cup of distilled water, and shake it to remove excess water. Wipe the wet cotton swab on your finger tips and then gently press the swab onto the agar side of the petri dish, streaking the plate with a zigzag motion as in Step ❸.

❻ Choose various surfaces to test for bacteria, such as a computer keyboard, bathroom doorknob, kitchen refrigerator handle, the finger tips of a sibling or parent, etc. Write the names of the surfaces in the following chart.

❼ When streaking the agar plates, remove them one at a time from the refrigerator. Keeping the petri dish agar side up, refer to your chart and label it with the name of one of the surfaces you will be testing.

❽ Repeat Step ❺, carefully testing each of the various surfaces you have chosen. The streaked petri dishes will not go back in the refrigerator.

❾ Incubate the plates by stacking them agar side up. Take the "Agar" petri dish out of the refrigerator and place it with the others. Leave the plates at room temperature for a week to ten days. [Note, do not put the plates back in the plastic sleeve. They need access to air for optimal growth.]

Results

In the following table, for each plate describe your results and make a drawing of any bacterial colonies you observe. Note whether there is growth visible on the two control plates labeled "Agar" and "Water."

Item Tested	Description	Illustration
Water (control)		
Agar (control)		
Hands		

BIOLOGY

III. Conclusions

Write your conclusions. Note that in this experiment you used two controls. One control tested the agar only and the other tested the water used during the experiment. Discuss how your controls impact the conclusions you can make.

_____

_____

_____

_____

_____

_____

_____

_____

_____

_____

_____

_____

_____

_____

_____

_____

BIOLOGY

IV. Why?

In this experiment you used agar plates to test for the presence of bacteria on your hands and household surfaces. Agar is made from seaweed and contains nutrients that allow for controlled bacterial growth. The agar should be sterile when it is initially poured into the petri dishes.

When you take a damp cotton swab and swipe it over a surface, it picks up a small amount of the bacteria that live on the surface. When you "streak" an agar plate by swiping the cotton swab in a zigzag motion across the agar, you spread a small amount of bacteria across the plate. During the incubation process, bacteria will grow on the agar plate.

By using controls you can determine if the agar on the plates or the water you used to dampen the cotton swab are contaminated with bacteria. By comparing the agar and water controls to the other plates you cultured, you are testing for contamination. If your controls show bacterial growth, you won't be able to determine the source of the bacteria on your other plates and the experiment will need to be repeated until your controls come back with negative or minimal bacterial growth. If you were performing this experiment in a science laboratory, everything would first be sterilized to kill any bacteria that might already be present.

V. Just For Fun

Retest the surfaces you tested that showed bacterial growth in your cultures. Wash each surface with a different household cleaner, and repeat the experiment. Try to determine how effective the different cleaners are at removing bacteria.

Record your results in the following table.

BIOLOGY

Item Tested and Cleaner Used	Description	Illustration

Experiment 10

It's the Law!

Introduction

Use the scientific method to determine Newton's First Law of Motion!

I. Think About It

❶ When you drive a car, can you choose to follow the speed limit? Why or why not?

_____

_____

_____

_____

_____

❷ Do you think laws like following the speed limit can be broken? Why or why not?

_____

_____

_____

_____

❸ When you throw a ball up, does it always come down? Why or why not?

_____

_____

_____

_____

_____

PHYSICS

❹ Do you think a ball will behave in the same way at the top of a mountain as it does at the bottom? Why or why not?

_____

_____

_____

_____

❺ Do you think a ball will behave in the same way on Earth and on the Moon? Why or why not?

_____

_____

_____

_____

_____

❻ Are there physical laws that can be broken? Why or why not?

_____

_____

_____

_____

II. Experiment 10: It's the Law!   Date _____

Objective   In this experiment we will use the scientific method to determine Newton's First Law of Motion.

Hypothesis _____

_____

_____

Materials

    tennis ball
    yarn or string (3 meters [10 ft])
    paperclip
    marble
    bouncing ball (1 or more)

EXPERIMENT

Part I

❶ Take the tennis ball outside and throw it as far as you can. Observe how the ball travels through the air. In the space below, sketch the path the ball traveled.

❷ Take the piece of string or yarn and attach it to the tennis ball as follows:

① Open the paperclip up on one side and make a hook on the end as shown below:

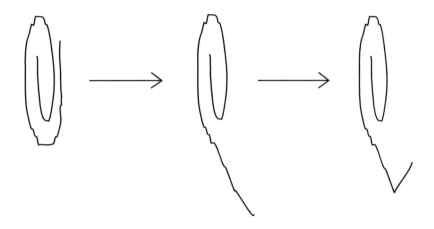

② Insert the hook on the end of the paperclip into the tennis ball by gently pushing and twisting.

③ Tie the string securely to the end of the paperclip.

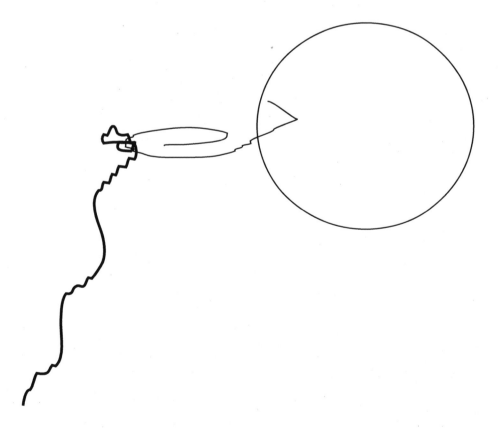

❸ Holding onto one end of the string, again throw the ball into the air as far as you can. Note how the ball travels, and in the space below, record what you see. Do this several times.

PHYSICS

Part II

❶ Take a marble and find a straight, clear path on a smooth area of the floor or outdoors. Roll the marble and record how it travels. Note where and how it stops or changes direction. Do this several times and record your observations in the next box.

❷ Repeat Step ❶ using a rough surface on which to roll the marble.

III. Conclusions

Based on your observations, what conclusions can you draw from the results of this experiment?

_____

_____

_____

_____

_____

_____

_____

_____

_____

_____

_____

_____

_____

_____

_____

_____

PHYSICS

IV. Why?

Physical laws are not laws we make up ourselves. The physical world is ordered, reliable, and consistent. This orderliness means there are underlying physical laws, or general principles, that we can discover to better understand the world. Physical laws are regularities that scientists have discovered in the way things behave. Physical laws are described by mathematics. Because the universe is ordered, mathematics can be used to precisely describe the laws that govern it.

In this experiment you discovered Newton's First Law of Motion by observing the movements of a tennis ball and a marble. Newton's First Law of Motion can be stated as: *A body will remain at rest or in motion until it is acted on by an outside force.*

By attaching one end of a long string to a tennis ball, you were able to observe a difference in how the ball traveled once it was thrown. The string changed the path the tennis ball followed. When the ball was thrown, it began traveling in an arc, but when the string reached its full length, the ball abruptly stopped and fell to the ground. The path the ball followed only changed when the string acted on it.

PHYSICS

In a similar way, when the marble was rolled on a smooth surface, it traveled in a mostly straight line. When the marble was rolled on a rough surface, the irregularities of the surface changed the path traveled by the marble. If you roll a marble on a smooth surface and the marble runs into an obstacle such as small building block, you will observe the marble traveling straight until it contacts the obstacle. The obstacle provides the outside force to act on the marble and change the path it's following. The marble's trajectory, or path, is not changed unless it is contacted by something—like a rough surface or a building block.

V. Just For Fun

Play with a rubber bouncing ball. Bounce it softly. How high does it go? Bounce it hard. How high does it go this time?

How many times can you get it to bounce if you drop it softly? How many times can you get it to bounce if you drop it hard?

What happens if you bounce it using the same amount of force but vary the height from which you drop it?

If you have a bouncing ball of a different size, repeat the experiment and observe any differences.

Record your observations.

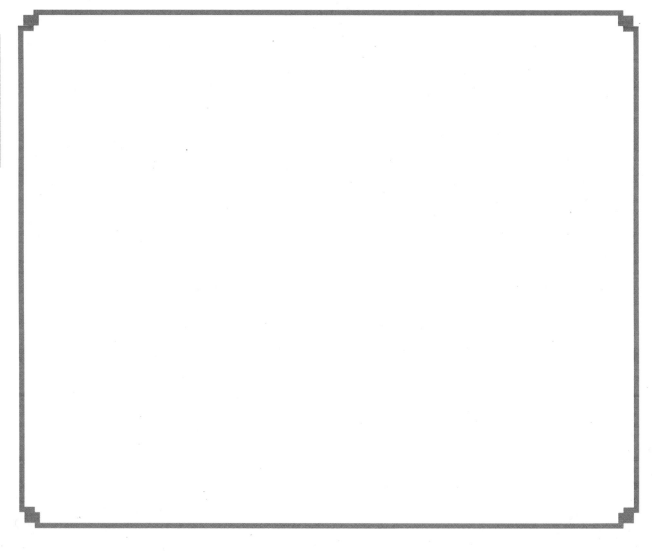

PHYSICS

Experiment 11

Fruit Works?

Introduction

Find out if fruit can do work!

I. Think About It

❶ Do you think if you and your brother or sister both carried the same box of books up the same flight of stairs, you would both be doing the same amount of work? Why or why not?

_____

_____

_____

_____

❷ Do you think you'd be doing the same amount of work if you carried a box of books up one flight of stairs and then carried a box of books weighing the same amount up two flights of stairs? Why or why not?

_____

_____

_____

_____

❸ If you and your friend each carried a box of books up the same flight of stairs, but your box weighted twice as much, would you both be doing the same amount of work? Why or why not?

_____

_____

_____

_____

PHYSICS

❹   Do you think a piece of fruit can do work? Why or why not?

_____

_____

_____

_____

❺   If you wanted a piece of fruit to do work for you, what would you have it do? Why?

_____

_____

_____

_____

❻   If fruit can do work, do you think a watermelon could do more work than a lemon? Why or why not?

_____

_____

_____

_____

PHYSICS

II. Experiment 11: Fruit Works?   Date _____

Objective _____

_____

Hypothesis _____

_____

_____

Materials

Slinky
several paperclips
1-2 apples
1-2 lemons or limes
1-2 oranges
1-2 bananas
spring balance scale or food scale
meterstick, yardstick, or tape measure
tape

EXPERIMENT

❶ Try to predict, just by "weighing" each piece of fruit in your hands, which piece of fruit will do the most work and which piece will do the least work on the spring that is in the scale.

❷ State your prediction as the hypothesis.

❸ Weigh each piece of fruit on the balance or food scale.

❹ Record the weights in the following chart.

Fruit	Weight (grams or ounces)

❺ Prepare the fruit for the experiment. Take a paperclip and stretch one side out to make a small hook like you did in Experiment 10. Place the hook in one of the pieces of fruit.

Repeat for each different kind of fruit you will be testing.

❻ Next, take the Slinky and hold it up to the level of your chest. Allow 10 to 15 coils to hang below your hand. You will have to hold most of the Slinky in your hand.

❼ Measure the distance from the floor to the bottom of the Slinky with the meterstick, yardstick, or tape measure. Record your result below.

Distance from floor to Slinky with no fruit attached

❽ Take a piece of fruit with a hook in it and attach it to the end of the Slinky. Hold the Slinky at the same height as in Step ❻ with the same number of coils hanging below your hand. Allow the Slinky to be pulled down by the fruit.

❾ Use the meterstick, yardstick, or tape measure to measure from the end of the Slinky to the floor. Record your results in the following chart in the *Distance Floor to Slinky (With Fruit)* column.

Fruit	Distance Floor to Slinky (With Fruit)	Distance Floor to Slinky (No Fruit)	Distance Extended

⑩   Repeat Steps ❽ and ❾ with different kinds of fruit. Record your results each time.

Results

❶   Using the above chart, in each row of the *Distance Floor to Slinky (No Fruit)* column, write the distance you recorded in Step ❼. Then subtract this distance from each of the distances you recorded in the *Distance Floor to Slinky (With Fruit)* column. This gives you the distance the Slinky was extended by each piece of fruit.

❷   Using the formula *work=distance x force* where force is the weight of the fruit, calculate the work each piece of fruit has done. Record your answers in the following chart.

Fruit	Work

III. Conclusions

What conclusions can you draw from your observations?

_____

_____

_____

_____

_____

_____

_____

_____

_____

_____

_____

_____

_____

_____

PHYSICS

IV. Why?

The concept of work may be difficult to understand because when we hear the word "work," we think of mowing the lawn or doing the laundry. However, in physics, work is defined as:

work = distance x force

By definition, a force is something that changes the position, shape, or speed of an object.

The illustration in the *Student Textbook* shows that, for the same amount of force, the work a short weight lifter does is less than the work a tall weight lifter does because the distance of the lift is less for the short weight lifter.

In this experiment, the heavier the fruit the more it stretched out the Slinky. The distance the fruit traveled was greater, so more work was done.

Another example: If you carry a box of books up one flight of stairs, and your brother carries the same box up two flights of stairs, who has done more work? Your brother because the books were carried a greater distance. In fact, your brother has done twice as much work because he carried the books twice as far.

If you carry a box of books up one flight of stairs, and your brother carries a box of books that weigh half as much up the same flight of stairs, you have done more work than your brother. In fact, you have done twice as much work.

In this experiment, by using the formula *work = distance x force* you found that the fruit that weighed the most did the most work.

V. Just For Fun

❶ What would happen if you attached two pieces of the same kind of fruit to the Slinky? How much work would be done?

Prediction _____

_____

_____

_____

❷ Test your prediction and calculate the work that was done by two pieces of fruit together. Record your data in the charts below.

Repeat this step one or more times using 2 pieces of fruit.

2 Pieces of Fruit	Weight	Distance: Floor to Slinky (With Fruit)	Distance Floor to Slinky (No Fruit)	Distance Extended

2 Pieces of Fruit	Work

Experiment 12

Smashed Banana

Introduction

Do you think a toy car can do work on a banana by gravitational potential energy being converted to kinetic energy? Try this experiment!

I. Think About It

❶ Do you think gravitational potential energy is useful? Why or why not?

_____

_____

_____

_____

_____

❷ What kinds of things can kinetic energy be used for?

_____

_____

_____

_____

❸ Do you think you use gravitational potential energy every day? If so, how?

_____

_____

_____

_____

PHYSICS

❹ Do you think you use kinetic energy every day? If so, how?

_____

_____

_____

_____

❺ What do you think would happen if gravitational potential energy could not
be converted?

_____

_____

_____

_____

❻ What would happen if there were no kinetic energy?

_____

_____

_____

_____

PHYSICS

II. Experiment 12: Smashed Banana

Date _____

Objective

_____

_____

Hypothesis

_____

_____

_____

Materials

small to medium size toy car
stiff cardboard
wooden board (more than 1 meter [3 feet] long)
straight pin or tack, several
small scale or balance
1 banana, sliced
10 pennies
meterstick, yardstick, or tape measure
tape

EXPERIMENT

❶ Read through all the steps of this experiment. Then write an objective and a hypothesis.

❷ Take a portion of the cardboard to make a backing for the banana slices. Using straight pins or tacks, attach two or three banana slices next to each other on the cardboard near the bottom.

❸ Use the wooden board to make a ramp. One end of the ramp should meet the banana slices. Your setup should look like the following illustration.

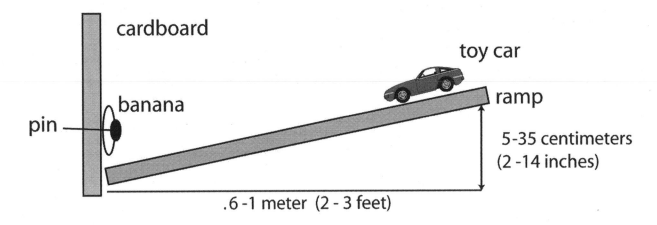

❹ Weigh the toy car with the scale or balance. Record your result.

Weight of toy car (grams or ounces) = _____

❺ Place the toy car on the ramp and elevate one end of the ramp 5 centimeters (2 inches). Allow the toy car to roll down the ramp and hit the banana. Record your results in the following chart.

❻ Elevate the ramp another 5 centimeters (2 inches). Now the ramp should be 10 centimeters (4 inches) off the ground. Allow the toy car to roll down the ramp and hit the banana. Record your results in the chart below

❼ Repeat, elevating the ramp 5 centimeters (2 inches) more each time. Record your results in the following chart.

Height (centimeters or inches)	Results (write your comments)
5 centimeters (2 inches)	
10 centimeters (4 inches)	
15 centimeters (6 inches)	
20 centimeters (8 inches)	
25 centimeters (10 inches)	
30 centimeters (12 inches)	
35 centimeters (14 inches)	

❽   What happened to the speed of the car as the ramp height increased?

_____

At which ramp height did the car smash the banana?

_____

❾   Now add 10 pennies to the toy car and weigh it again. Repeat the previous steps, rolling the toy car with the pennies on it down the ramp and elevating the ramp 5 centimeters (2 inches) more each time Record your results.

Weight of toy car plus 10 pennies (grams or ounces) = _____

Height (centimeters or inches)	Results (write your comments)
5 centimeters (2 inches)	
10 centimeters (4 inches)	
15 centimeters (6 inches)	
20 centimeters (8 inches)	
25 centimeters (10 inches)	
30 centimeters (12 inches)	
35 centimeters (14 inches)	

❿   At which ramp height did the car smash the banana? _____

Was the banana smashed at the same height by the light car and the heavy car? _____

If "no," which car needed to be at a greater height to smash the banana?

_____

PHYSICS

Results

Calculate the GPE for the height of the ramp at which the toy car—with and without the 10 pennies—smashed the banana. Use the equation:

gravitational potential energy (GPE) = weight x height

Record your answers below.

GPE for car without pennies _____

GPE for car with pennies _____

Is the GPE the same (or close to the same) for both cars? _____

PHYSICS

III. Conclusions

What conclusions can you draw from your observations?

_____

_____

_____

_____

_____

_____

_____

_____

_____

_____

_____

_____

_____

_____

_____

PHYSICS

IV. Why?

Energy exists in different forms and is converted from one form to another. In this experiment you used the conversion of two different types of energy—potential energy and kinetic energy—to do work when the toy car smashed a banana. Potential energy is energy that has the potential to do work, and kinetic energy is the energy of motion. The gravitational potential energy (GPE) of the toy car on the elevated ramp was converted into kinetic energy (KE) as the toy car moved down the ramp.

The amount of GPE an object has is equal to the amount of work that was needed to lift the object to its current position. Each time you raised the ramp, you added more GPE to the toy car. The higher you lifted the ramp, the more GPE the toy car had and the more KE it had as the GPE was converted

Kinetic energy is proportional to both the weight of the object and its speed. Heavier objects will have more KE at a given speed than lighter objects, and slower objects will have less KE at a given weight than faster objects. When you put pennies on the toy car, it was heavier and moved faster and so gained KE.

Recall that work is the force of an object multiplied by the distance the object is moved. We know that an object having kinetic energy is moving, and if it hits another object, it can cause the object it hits to move or change shape. There is work done when potential energy is converted into kinetic energy and when kinetic energy is converted into other forms of energy, such as heat and sound. The work done on an object equals the change in kinetic energy of that object. When the moving toy car contacted the banana, the kinetic energy was converted into other forms of energy and work was done to the banana.

Potential energy is useful only when it gets converted to another form of energy. Energy is neither created nor destroyed—but only converted from one form to anther.

PHYSICS

V. Just For Fun

What happens if you replace the banana with a raw egg? Do you need more or less gravitational force to smash an egg than a banana?

Record your observations.

Observations of a Smashed Egg

PHYSICS

Experiment 13

On Your Own

Introduction

Create your own experiment to explore the conversion of energy.

I. Think About It

❶ Do you think potential energy can be used without converting it to another form of energy? Why or why not?

_____

_____

_____

_____

❷ Do you think an object could go back and forth between having gravitational potential energy and kinetic energy? Why or why not?

_____

_____

_____

_____

PHYSICS

❸ Do you think you could gather energy from the Sun and use it? Why or why not?

_____

_____

_____

_____

❹ Do you think you use energy from chemical reactions during the day? Why or why not?

_____

_____

_____

_____

❺ What do you think life would be like if we did not have fossil fuels?

_____

_____

_____

_____

❻ Do you think water can have energy? Why or why not?

_____

_____

_____

_____

PHYSICS

II. Experiment 13: On Your Own

This time you get to design your own experiment. The goal is to convert as many forms of energy as you can into other forms of energy. You can use any type of energy conversion more than once.

Example:

A scenario can be designed in which energy is used to put out a fire. A marble is rolled down a ramp and bumps into a domino that has on top of it a small cap containing baking soda. A chemical reaction is started when the baking soda falls into vinegar, which produces carbon dioxide gas that puts out the fire.

In this case, the marble begins with gravitational potential energy that is converted to kinetic energy as the marble rolls. The kinetic energy of the rolling marble is used to convert gravitational potential energy into kinetic energy (the falling baking soda) which then starts a chemical reaction.

Using Energy to Put Out a Fire

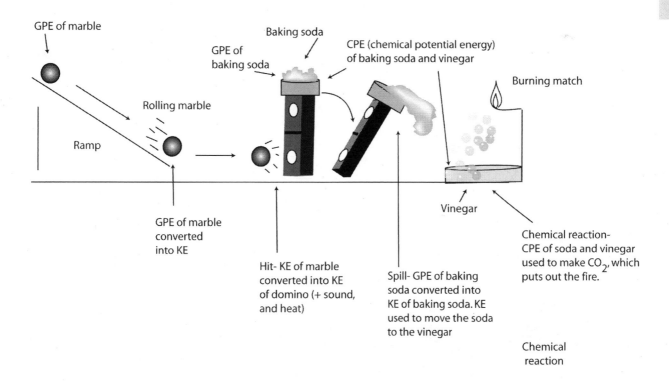

Use the following guide to design your experiment:

❶ Write down as many different forms of energy as you can think of.

kinetic energy _____   _____

_____   _____

_____   _____

❷ Write down different ways each of these forms of energy can be represented.

Form of Energy	Represented by	Represented by	Represented by
kinetic energy	rolling marble	moving toy car	moving ball

PHYSICS

❸ Write down different ways to connect two or more of these forms of energy and explain how one form will be converted into another.

---

moving toy car bumps into marble and starts it rolling

(kinetic energy converts potential energy into kinetic energy)

---

❹ Design an experiment to convert energy from one form into another. Give your experiment a title and write an objective and a hypothesis. Write down the materials you will need, and then write down the steps you will take to collect the results. Draw your setup. See how many different forms of energy you can convert. Perform the experiment, making careful observations. Draw conclusions based on what you observe.

Experiment: _____   Date _____

Objective _____

_____

Hypothesis _____

_____

_____

Materials _____ _____ _____

_____ _____ _____

_____ _____ _____

_____ _____ _____

EXPERIMENT

_____

_____

_____

_____

_____

_____

_____

_____

PHYSICS

PHYSICS

PHYSICS

III. Conclusions

What conclusions can you draw from your observations?

_____

_____

_____

_____

_____

_____

_____

_____

_____

_____

_____

_____

_____

_____

_____

IV. Why?

The law of conservation of energy states that energy is never created or destroyed but only converted from one form to another. In this experiment you took several different types of energy, and by connecting them, converted energy from one form to another. For example, if you used a marble to knock down a popsicle stick covered in baking soda and the baking soda then fell into a thimble full of vinegar, you converted kinetic and potential energy into chemical and heat energy. By converting energy from one form to another, you showed the law of conservation of energy in action.

V. Just For Fun

Based on what you learned in your experiment, create another experiment with a different series of events that convert energy. How many different steps can you include in your setup? List them below and draw your experimental setup on the next page. Once you have completed your setup, perform the experiment.

PHYSICS

Energy Conversion Steps

_____

_____

_____

_____

_____

_____

_____

_____

Experimental Setup

III. Conclusions

What conclusions can you draw from your observations of this experiment?
Compare your two experiments. Was one easier to perform? Why or why not?
Did what you learned in the first experiment help you plan the second one?
Why or why not?

_____

_____

_____

_____

_____

_____

_____

_____

_____

_____

_____

_____

_____

PHYSICS

Experiment 14

Observing Your World

Photo Credit: US Geological Survey/by Lyn Topinka

Introduction

Do you think if you go outside and look carefully, you will see things you haven't noticed before? Try it!

I. Think About It

❶ What features do you think you will see when you go outside?

_____

_____

_____

_____

❷ What do you think the dirt in your yard or in the park looks like?

_____

_____

_____

_____

❸ What geological features do you see when you go to the grocery store?

_____

_____

_____

_____

GEOLOGY

❹ What man-made features do you see when you go to the grocery store?

_____

_____

_____

_____

❺ In what ways does the weather change where you live? Do you think any changes in the weather affect the landscape?

_____

_____

_____

_____

❻ Do you think places such as a city or a rural area have a history? Why or why not?

_____

_____

_____

_____

GEOLOGY

II. Experiment 14: Observing Your World   Date _____

Objective _____

_____

Hypothesis _____

_____

_____

Materials

> pencil, pen, colored pencils
> small jar
> trowel or spoon
> binoculars (optional)

EXPERIMENT

❶ Step outside your front or back door and walk until your feet are on some type of ground (dirt, grass, or concrete).

❷ Observe where you are. Are you in a city? Are you in the country? Use the space below to draw or write what you see.

GEOLOGY

❸ Observe any geological features near you. Do you see mountains? Do you see lakes or rivers? Do you see the ocean? Do you see other geological features? Record what you are observing.

❹ Use the trowel to collect a small sample of dirt. (If you live in the city, walk to a park or some other place where you can collect a dirt sample.)

❺ Observe the dirt sample. Is it light in color? Dark? Does it contain small rocks? Large rocks? Does it have any organic matter (living things, such as grass or bugs)? Record what you observe.

GEOLOGY

❻ Observe any man-made structures. Do you see buildings? Roads? Bridges? Other man-made structures? Record what you see.

❼ Observe any dynamic features in your area including the weather. Do you get earthquakes? Do you live near a volcano? Does it rain frequently, or do you get very little rain where you live? Do you have tornadoes, hurricanes, or severe snow storms?

GEOLOGY

❽ Think about the area in which you live. What is its history? How long has it looked the way it looks today? If you are in a city, how long has the city been there? What do you think it looked like before there were buildings, roads, or other structures? Write your observations below.

_____

_____

_____

_____

_____

_____

_____

_____

_____

_____

_____

_____

_____

_____

GEOLOGY

Results

Assemble your data in the chart below.

Data Describing Where I Live	
Geological Features	
Soil Type	
Man-made structures	
Dynamic Processes	
Weather	
History	

GEOLOGY

III. Conclusions

Review the observations you made during this experiment. What did you observe that you had not noticed before? Do you think that taking the time to look at things carefully makes a difference in what you observe? Why or why not?

_____

_____

_____

_____

_____

_____

_____

_____

_____

_____

_____

_____

_____

_____

GEOLOGY

IV. Why?

The first step towards understanding the world around you is to observe it. Before you can know what the world looks like, how it changes, and how the different parts work together, you have to go outside and observe buildings, rocks, the soil, clouds, sunlight, plants, and animals. You need to observe the weather, how it changes, and how it affects the landscape and living things. Observations made over time are important for noticing how living things and their activities change with the seasons. Even though you may "think" you know what the world around you looks like, you don't actually know until you observe it. Also, the world around you changes daily, weekly, monthly, and yearly.

If you live in the city, buildings are constructed, torn down, and rebuilt. Weather fades colors that were once brightly painted. Trees grow and fall down. Grass grows and is mowed. In the country, fields are plowed and crops grow and are harvested. Animals have babies that grow to be adults. Storms create rivers, and snow and ice melt, sometimes creating floods.

By observing the world around you, you can learn about how geology works. The world becomes more interesting when you pay attention to what things look like, how they change, and how they stay the same.

V. Just For Fun

Imagine you got an email from someone on the planet Alpha Centauri Bb. They have never been to Earth, and they ask you what Earth is like. Using the data you have collected, write a narrative (story) describing what the area is like where you live. Include enough detail that the Alpha Centaurian can form a mental image of your surroundings.

GEOLOGY

Email to an Alpha Centaurian

Mineral Properties

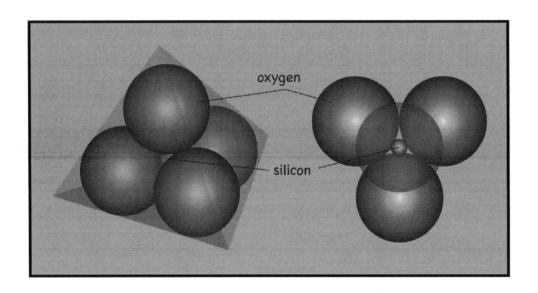

Introduction

Explore using scientific tests to identify minerals.

I. Think About It

❶ What do you think dirt (soil) is made of? Why?

_____

_____

_____

_____

❷ Do you think soil everywhere on Earth is the same? Why or why not?

_____

_____

_____

_____

❸ What do you think rocks are made of? Why?

_____

_____

_____

_____

GEOLOGY

❹ Do you think if you went outside with a shovel, you could dig up some minerals? Why or why not?

_____

_____

_____

_____

_____

❺ Do you think minerals can be used to make artworks? Why or why not?

_____

_____

_____

_____

_____

❻ Do you think there are ways to tell one mineral from another? Why or why not?

_____

_____

_____

_____

_____

GEOLOGY

II. Experiment 15: Mineral Properties   Date _____

Objective   _____

_____

Hypothesis   _____

_____

_____

Materials

known mineral samples:
    calcite, feldspar, quartz, hematite
several rocks from your backyard or near your home
copper penny
steel nail
streak plate (unglazed white ceramic tile)
paper
scissors
marking pen
tape
vinegar
lemon juice
eyedropper or spoon

EXPERIMENT—Part I

▶ The hardness of a mineral is determined by its resistance to being scratched. The Mohs scale of mineral hardness lists the relative hardness of ten common minerals and also various objects that can be used in scratch testing minerals.

Test the hardness of the known mineral samples shown in the materials list by using the objects listed in the Mohs hardness scale on the next page. Fill in the chart on the next page with your test results and the appearance of the sample (color, texture, size, etc.).

Results

Mohs Scale of Mineral Hardness	
Object	**Hardness**
fingernail	2.5
copper penny	3
steel nail	5.5
streak plate	6.5

Mineral Name	Hardness	Appearance
Calcite		
Quartz		
Feldspar		
Hematite		

GEOLOGY

EXPERIMENT—Part II

▶ Do a streak test for each of the known minerals. Take each mineral sample and rub it firmly across the streak plate.

Results

Record the streak color of each mineral sample.

Mineral Name	Streak Color	Notes
Calcite		
Quartz		
Feldspar		
Hematite		

EXPERIMENT—Part III

❶ Go to the backyard or other place nearby and collect several rocks that look different from each other in color and texture.

❷ Using paper and tape or some other method, label the rocks you collected. Use a different number to identify each rock. Record the numbers in the following chart.

❸ Using the Mohs scale of mineral hardness, do a scratch test to find out the hardness of each unknown sample. Next do a streak test.

❹ Record your results. Review your results from Part I and Part II and see if you can tell what mineral is in your rock sample.

Results

Rock #	Hardness	Streak Color	Possible Mineral

GEOLOGY

III. Conclusions

In this experiment you tested the hardness and streak color of known and unknown minerals. By comparing your results from Parts 1-III of the experiment, were you able to determine the type of mineral or minerals that are in the rocks you collected near your home? Why or why not? Record your conclusions.

_____

_____

_____

_____

_____

_____

_____

_____

_____

_____

_____

_____

_____

The hardness test using the Mohs hardness scale and the streak test are "subjective" tests. That is, the outcome may vary depending on the type of ceramic tile used for the streak plate, the type of nail or penny, and individual interpretations of results.

Another way to test for the type of mineral is to use chemical analysis. An acid test uses hydrochloric acid to test for calcium carbonate. Minerals containing calcium carbonate will effervesce (bubble or foam) when acid is used to create a chemical reaction. Do you think this is a more objective type of test? Why or why not? Write your answers below.

_____

_____

_____

_____

_____

_____

_____

_____

_____

_____

_____

GEOLOGY

IV. Why?

In the same way that different plastics are made of different molecules that make them harder or softer and different colors, minerals made of different atoms and molecules will be harder or softer and different colors. The Mohs scale of mineral hardness is a quick and easy test used by geologists to help determine the type of minerals in a sample. The streak color and the acid test are also quick ways to help with mineral identification. The materials used to perform these tests are easily carried in a backpack out in the field.

By using simple tests and observations, field geologists can quickly determine if the rocks in an area are most likely limestone, granite, mica, or feldspar. Samples can be taken back to the lab for a more complete analysis requiring more complicated equipment.

V. Just For Fun

Use vinegar to test your rock and mineral collection to see if any samples have a chemical reaction with the acid. Use an eyedropper or spoon to apply the liquid. Record your results in the following chart.

Now use lemon juice to test your mineral collection for a chemical reaction. Record your results.

Compare your results. Did your samples react the same way to the vinegar as they did to the lemon juice? Why?

Look online or at the library to find out how your known minerals would be expected to react with acids. Did your known minerals react in the expected way? Why or why not?

GEOLOGY

Acid Test

Mineral	Vinegar Reaction?	Lemon Reaction?	Expected Reaction & Notes
Calcite			
Quartz			
Feldspar			
Hematite			
Rock # ___			
Rock # ___			
Rock # ___			
Rock # ___			
Rock # ___			

Experiment 16

Model Earth

Introduction

Explore Earth's layers by building a model.

I. Think About It

❶ Do you think scientists will ever be able to get actual samples from all the different layers of the Earth? Why or why not?

_____

_____

_____

_____

❷ What do you think it would be like if the Earth were solid rock all the way to the core and there were no different layers?

_____

_____

_____

_____

❸ Do you think by studying rocks geologists can learn anything about the interior of Earth? Why or why not?

_____

_____

_____

_____

GEOLOGY

❹ Do you think there are living things in the asthenosphere? Why or why not?

_____

_____

_____

_____

❺ What do you think Earth would be like if there were no crust or lithosphere?

_____

_____

_____

_____

❻ How do you think advances in technology have allowed us to discover more about the structure of Earth?

_____

_____

_____

_____

GEOLOGY

II. Experiment 16: Model Earth   Date _____

Objective _____

_____

Hypothesis _____

_____

_____

Materials

_____

_____

_____

_____

_____

GEOLOGY

EXPERIMENT

In this experiment you will decide how to build an accurate model of Earth. Scientists use models to help them understand how things work. Creating accurate models is an important skill when doing science. The more accurately a model depicts reality, the more scientists can learn about how things work.

❶ On the following page, list what you know about Earth's layers. Record features such as whether scientists believe the layer is soft or rigid, solid or liquid, rock or iron. Also record the depth of the layer and any other features the layer may exhibit.

Use the *Student Textbook,* internet, and/or library to collect your information.

Features of Earth's Layers

Layer	Depth	Features
Crust		
Lithosphere		
Asthenosphere		
Mesosphere		
Inner Core		
Outer Core		

❷ Using the chart that you created on the previous page, go through the information you collected about each layer. Think about what material you could use to accurately represent each layer. Record the materials in the chart below.

Model Materials

Layer	Materials
Crust	
Lithosphere	
Asthenosphere	
Mesosphere	
Inner Core	
Outer Core	

❸ Decide which layers of Earth you will represent in your model. In the Materials section on the first page of this experiment, list the materials you will use for your model.

❹ Assemble a model of Earth using these materials.

GEOLOGY

Results

❶ Review your model and observe how well it represents Earth's geology.

❷ In the chart below write your observations about how accurately your model depicts the overall architecture of Earth and the characteristics of each layer.

Model Results

Questions	Observations
Does your model have layers? Which ones? Describe each layer.	
Do the layers represent accurate depths in your model? How do you know?	
Do the layers represent accurate consistency? (For example, is the lithosphere rigid and the mesosphere soft?)	
Do the layers in the model accurately represent the change that occurs at the boundary between each of the layers? Why or why not?	

III. Conclusions

Based on your observations, evaluate the accuracy of your model. How easy or difficult was it to accurately represent Earth's different layers?

_____

_____

_____

_____

_____

_____

_____

_____

_____

_____

_____

_____

_____

_____

GEOLOGY

IV. Why?

In this chapter you explored how to build an accurate model of Earth. As you know, model building is an important part of doing science. Models help scientists understand how things work. However, it is not always easy to build accurate models. For example, Earth is much too large to build a model of the exact same size as Earth. Also, scientists don't know for sure what layers below the crust look like, so building an accurate model of Earth is difficult. Parts of the model will be accurate and other parts will most likely be inaccurate.

As scientists learn more and more about Earth's layers, better and more accurate models will be developed.

V. Just For Fun

Make another model of Earth, but this time make one you can eat!

CHOCOLATE LAVA CAKE

butter   113 grams (1/2 cup)
semi-sweet chocolate chips   133 ml (1/2 cup + 1 Tbsp.)
2 whole eggs
2 egg yolks
powdered sugar   192 ml (3/4 cup + 1 Tbsp.)
flour   94 ml (1/3 cup + 1 Tbsp.)

Microwave butter briefly until melted. Stir in chocolate chips until melted. Mix in whole eggs and yolks, then powdered sugar. Stir in flour. Pour into custard cups thoroughly greased with butter. Bake at 190° C (375° F) until edges are set and centers are still soft, about 10-13 minutes. Don't overbake. Makes about 4.

Can you think of any food items you can add to represent the Earth's crust and inner core?

On the next page record the accuracy of this model and then compare it your first model.

GEOLOGY

Model Results and Comparisons

GEOLOGY

Experiment 17

Dynamic Earth

Introduction

Explore plate tectonics with this experiment.

I. Think About It

❶ What do you think Earth would be like if the lithosphere were one solid piece instead of being broken into plates?

_____

_____

_____

_____

_____

❷ What do you think would happen if there were no convection in the soft layers of Earth?

_____

_____

_____

_____

_____

❸ What do you think would happen if all lava were the same viscosity?

_____

_____

_____

_____

GEOLOGY

❹ What do you think Earth would be like if there were no earthquakes and volcanoes?

_____

_____

_____

_____

❺ What do you think you might learn by studying the ground after an earthquake?

_____

_____

_____

_____

❻ What do you think you might learn by observing a volcano erupting?

_____

_____

_____

_____

GEOLOGY

II. Experiment 17: Dynamic Earth

Date _____

Objective _____

_____

Hypothesis _____

_____

_____

Materials

- brittle candy (recipe below)
- 1 jar smooth peanut butter
- 118 ml (1/2 cup) crushed graham crackers

EXPERIMENT

❶ Use the following instructions to make brittle candy.

Brittle Candy Recipe

Ingredients

237 ml (1 cup) white sugar
118 ml (1/2 cup) light corn syrup
1.25 ml (1/4 teaspoon) salt
59 ml (1/4 cup) water
28 grams (2 Tbsp) butter, softened
5 ml (1 teaspoon) baking soda

Equipment

2 liter (2 qt) saucepan
candy thermometer
cookie sheet, approx. 30x36
   cm (12x14 inches)
2 spatulas

GEOLOGY

Brittle Candy Recipe—Instructions

Grease a large cookie sheet.

Measure sugar, corn syrup, salt, and water into a heavy 2 liter (2 quart) saucepan. Bring mixture to a boil over medium heat.

Stir until the sugar is dissolved.

Put the candy thermometer in the saucepan and continue cooking.

Stir frequently. The candy should be done when the temperature reaches 150° C (300° F). You can check whether it is done by dropping a small amount of the hot candy mixture into very cold water. If the candy separates into hard and brittle threads, it is done cooking.

Remove from heat and quickly stir in butter and baking soda.

Pour at once onto the greased cookie sheet and spread the mixture into a rectangle of about 30x36 centimeters (12x14 inches). You can use two buttered spatulas to spread the candy.

Allow to cool. Break the candy into large pieces.

❷ Spread a 1.25 cm (1/2 inch) thick layer of peanut butter on a plate or another cookie sheet.

❸ Mix 118 ml (1/2 cup) of crushed graham crackers with 59 ml (1/4 cup) of peanut butter.

❹ Take 2 large pieces of brittle candy and spread the peanut butter/graham cracker mixture on top of each of them.

❺ Place the two pieces of brittle candy (peanut butter/graham cracker side up) about 2.5-5 cm (1-2 inches) apart on top of the peanut butter that is on the plate or cookie sheet.

GEOLOGY

❻ In the following chart write which layer each food item represents (the asthenosphere, the lithosphere, or the crust).

Earth's Layers Represented

Item	Earth's Layer
Peanut Butter	
Brittle Candy	
Graham Cracker/Peanut Butter Mixture	

❼ Gently holding the sides of the brittle candy pieces, move the candy around on top of the peanut butter and observe what happens.

Have the pieces bump into each other, scrape alongside each other, and move up or down with respect to each other.

Move the pieces quickly and slowly and observe the difference. Try to get one piece to slide under the other piece and observe what happens to the graham cracker topping.

❽ In the box on the next page, write about what you observe during this experiment. Think about what you have learned about plate tectonics and how your model relates to what you know.

GEOLOGY

Plate Tectonics Model—Observations

Results

Review your observations and answer the questions in the following chart. Note what happened to the lower peanut butter layer, the brittle candy pieces, and the top graham cracker/peanut butter layer.

Tectonic Plates Model Results

Questions	Observations
What happened when you moved the brittle candy pieces slowly on top of the peanut butter?	
What happened when you moved the brittle candy pieces quickly on top of the peanut butter?	
What happened when you collided two brittle candy pieces together?	
What happened when you moved the pieces up or down with respect to each other?	
What happened when you slid the two pieces side by side in different directions?	

GEOLOGY

III. Conclusions

What conclusions can you draw from your observations?

Based on your observations and results, explain what you think happens when two of Earth's plates collide with each other, slide past each other, or move up and down with respect to each other. Do you think your model was a good representation of plate tectonics? Why or why not?

_____

_____

_____

_____

_____

_____

_____

_____

_____

_____

_____

_____

GEOLOGY

IV. Why?

Earth is a dynamic planet, meaning it is constantly changing. Features of Earth's surface can be changed quickly by natural phenomena, such as sudden earthquakes and volcanic activity. There are also changes that occur over very long periods of time, such as the formation of river valleys, the wearing away of land forms by glaciers, and the growth of mountains due to forces caused by the movement of tectonic plates.

Plate tectonics is a theory that has been proposed to explain how earthquakes, mountain ridges, and volcanoes occur. Although scientists can't directly sample the layers below the Earth's crust, by putting together pieces of information they obtain by making observations, they can propose a theory to explain dynamic phenomena. Scientists can draw conclusions based on data from observations such as the location, age, and activity of volcanoes; analysis of the composition and deformation of rock in mountains; and the location, type, and strength of earthquakes.

According to the theory of plate tectonics, earthquakes occur when two plates collide with, push on, or slide past each other, causing stresses to build up along the plate boundaries and also in the interior of the plates. Earthquakes occur along faults, or fractures, in the Earth's surface. The most active faults are at or near plate boundaries, such as the San Andreas Fault in California. But there are also some active areas within plate interiors, such as the New Madrid Seismic Zone located in the Mississippi Valley.

The movement of plates can cause mountains to form as land masses are pushed together causing the land to fold. Mountains can also be formed as the movement of plates causes big blocks of land to move up and down.

Although the model in this experiment is not a perfect representation, it is helpful in visualizing how the layers and forces within the Earth work to create earthquakes and form mountains.

V. Just For Fun

Using the internet or the library, research various ways to create a model volcano. Choose a method and write your own experiment.

Experiment 17: Model Volcano

Date _____

Objective   _____

_____

Hypothesis   _____

_____

_____

Materials

_____

_____

_____

_____

EXPERIMENT

_____

_____

_____

_____

_____

_____

EXPERIMENT (continued)

Model Volcano

III. Conclusions

Constellations

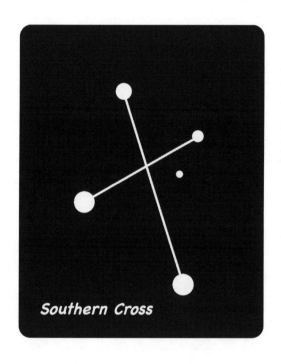

Southern Cross

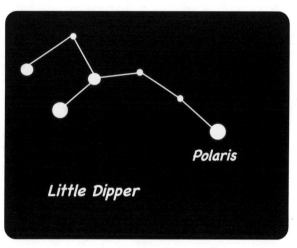

Little Dipper

Polaris

Introduction

Find some constellations and see if you can use the stars to tell which direction you are going.

I. Think About It

❶ Do you think it was important for ancient people to be able to recognize different stars? Why or why not?

_____

_____

_____

_____

❷ Why do think a star is in a different place in the sky in the morning than at night?

_____

_____

_____

_____

❸ Do you think stars move from one constellation into another? Why or why not?

_____

_____

_____

_____

ASTRONOMY

❹ Do you think people are discovering new constellations all the time? Why or why not?

_____

_____

_____

_____

❺ If you are in the Northern Hemisphere and you find the North Star pointing to north, how would you find south?

_____

_____

_____

_____

❻ Do you think sailors were able to find their way at sea before compasses were invented? Why or why not?

_____

_____

_____

_____

ASTRONOMY

II. Experiment 18: Constellations

Date _____

Objective _____

_____

Hypothesis _____

_____

_____

Materials

pencil
flashlight
compass

A clear night sky away from bright lights is needed.

EXPERIMENT

Record your physical location, city, state, or country, whether you are in the Northern or Southern Hemisphere, and the month.

Location	
Hemisphere	
Month	

ASTRONOMY

Northern Hemisphere

❶ In the evening on a clear night away from city lights go outside and, without using a compass, locate "north." To do this you will need to find the Big Dipper. The Big Dipper is a set of stars that form the shape of a "dipping spoon." (The Big Dipper is not an official constellation but is called an *asterism*—a small group of stars.) The two stars on the end of the dipping spoon point to the star Polaris.

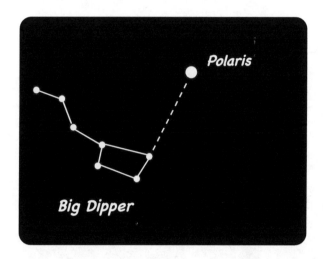

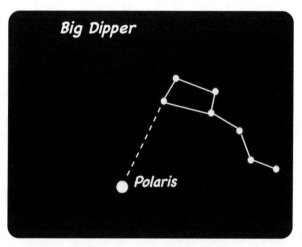

Polaris is the "North Star," and when you turn towards Polaris, you are pointing "north." It doesn't matter how the Big Dipper is oriented in the sky, the two end stars always point to the North Star. The North Star is the only star in the sky that doesn't move (much). All of the constellations appear to move around the North Star. Once you find the North Star you can find nearby constellations.

❷ Now that you have found the North Star, try to find the constellation called the "Little Dipper."

Polaris forms the end of the handle of the Little Dipper.

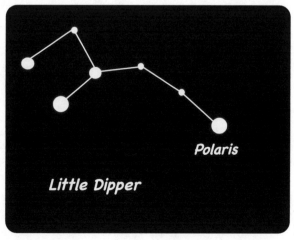

❸ In the following box, draw the Little Dipper as it looks to you.

Little Dipper

❹ Try to locate the "Dragon." The Dragon constellation is between the Big Dipper and Little Dipper.

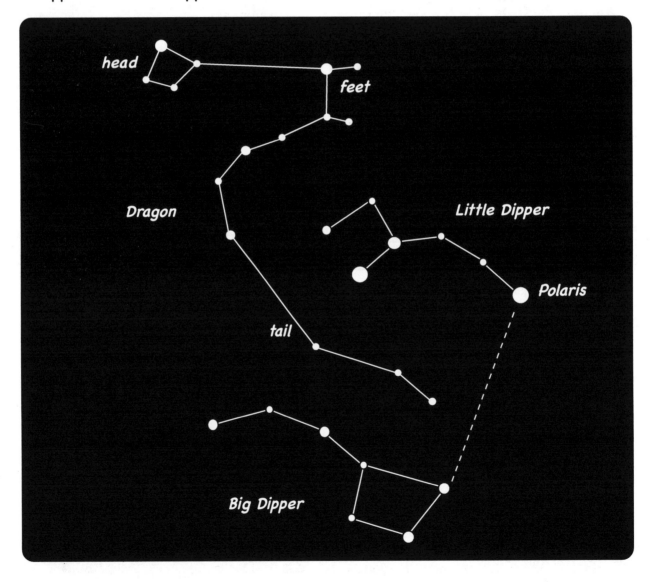

❺ On the following page, draw the Dragon constellation as you see it.

ASTRONOMY

Draw the Dragon constellation as you observe it.

❻ Count the stars in the Dragon constellation in the image on the previous page. Compare this number with the number of stars you've recorded for the Dragon. Are they the same? Why or why not?

_____

_____

_____

❼ Find the North Star again and use your compass to see if the North Star really is above the North Pole.

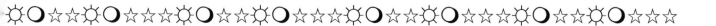

EXPERIMENT

Southern Hemisphere

The South Pole doesn't have a star directly over it like the North Pole does, but you can still find south using the stars.

❶   In the evening on a clear night away from city lights go outside. Look toward the south to find the Southern Cross constellation, also called Crux. It is a small, bright constellation of four stars that are close together. You may see two crosses near each other. The Southern Cross is smaller and has brighter stars. it also has a dimmer fifth star tucked in between two of its arms. The larger, dimmer cross is called the False Cross and is an asterism rather than a constellation.

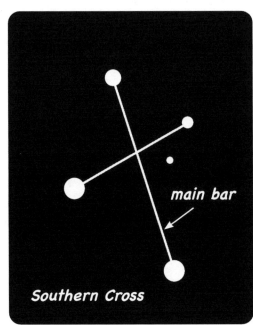

❷   While looking at the Southern Cross, follow with your eyes the main bar of the cross (the line between the two stars that are farthest apart).

❸   Now imagine you are extending the main bar downward and adding 4 1/2 times to its length. By doing this you will arrive at a point in the sky called the South Celestial Pole which is directly above the South Pole.

❹   From the South Celestial Pole, lower your eyes straight down to the horizon. The point you are looking at will be south.

❺   Using your compass, see how close you came to finding south.

❻   Record your results on the next page.

Results - Finding south by using the Southern Cross

_____

_____

_____

_____

_____

_____

_____

❼ See if you can find both the Southern Cross and the False Cross and then draw them as you see them.

The Southern Cross and the False Cross

III. Conclusions

Summarize how easy or difficult it was to find the constellations you were looking for. Do you think you could use these stars for navigation? What role, if any, does your physical location and the month you made these observations have on your results? What did you observe about the night sky that you hadn't noticed before?

_____

_____

_____

_____

_____

_____

_____

_____

_____

_____

_____

_____

_____

_____

_____

IV. Why?

In ancient times people were very observant of the world around them. There were no city lights, so they could see the stars very clearly. They noticed that there was one star that didn't seem to change position over the course of the night and that all the other stars seemed to rotate around it. This star is now called the North Star.

Before the invention of the compass, people in the Northern Hemisphere were able to determine in which direction they were traveling at night by looking at the position of the North Star. If it was directly in front of them, they were going north; directly behind them, they were going south; to the right of them, they were going west; and to the left of them, they were going east.

Although the Southern Cross is not directly over the South Pole, ancient people discovered how it could be used in a similar manner to determine which way was south. Then the other directions could be found.

The International Astronomical Union (IAU) is an organization that holds meetings where astronomers from all over the world can get together to share ideas and research. The IAU is also the organization that gives official names to celestial bodies that are discovered. The IAU decided that it would be helpful to have an official set of constellations and in 1930 came up with the current list of 88 constellations. Half of these constellations come from the ancient Greeks who described them long ago.

ASTRONOMY

V. Just For Fun

Use online or library resources to find more constellations that you can see from the area where you live. Pick your favorite three constellations. Go outside on a clear night, find the constellations, and draw them as you see them.

Favorite Constellations

Lunar and Solar Eclipses

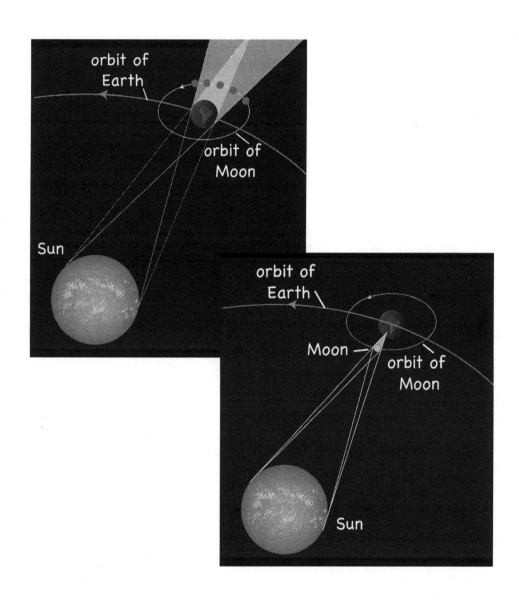

Introduction

Use a model to see how lunar and solar eclipses are created.

I. Think About It

❶ What do you think people learned about the Earth, Moon, and Sun by observing eclipses? Why?

_____

_____

_____

_____

_____

❷ Do you think there would be solar eclipses if Earth did not have a Moon? Why or why not?

_____

_____

_____

_____

❸ Do you think there would be eclipses if the Moon did not orbit Earth but always stayed in the same position above Earth? Why or why not?

_____

_____

_____

_____

ASTRONOMY

❹ Do you think there is a lunar eclipse every time the Moon is on the opposite side of Earth from the Sun? Why or why not?

_____

_____

_____

_____

❺ Do you think when there is a solar eclipse, everyone on the side of Earth facing the Sun will be able to see the solar eclipse? Why or why not?

_____

_____

_____

_____

❻ If you were living at a space station on the Moon, do you think you would see any eclipses? Why or why not?

_____

_____

_____

_____

ASTRONOMY

II. Experiment 19: Lunar and Solar Eclipses   Date _____

Objective _____

_____

Hypothesis _____

_____

_____

Materials

basketball
ping-pong ball
flashlight
empty toilet paper tube
tape
scissors
a dark room

EXPERIMENT

In this experiment you will observe how lunar and solar eclipses occur.

❶ In a dark room, place the basketball on top of one end of a toilet paper tube that is sitting upright on the floor. The toilet paper tube will hold the basketball in place.

❷ Holding the flashlight, stand several feet away from the basketball. Turn on the flashlight and point it towards the basketball. Lay the flashlight on the floor in a position that keeps the basketball illuminated.

❸ Hold the ping-pong ball so that it is between the flashlight and the illuminated basketball. Adjust the position of the ping-pong ball until you can see its shadow on the basketball.

ASTRONOMY

❹ Move the ping-pong ball up until there is no shadow on the basketball.

❺ Now lower the ping-pong ball until there is no shadow on the basketball.

❻ Move the ping-pong ball in an "orbit" around the basketball. Observe where the ping-pong ball needs to be in order for it to cast a shadow on the basketball and where the ping-pong ball needs to be for the basketball to cast a shadow on the ping-pong ball. Also note the position of the ping-pong ball when no shadows are cast.

Results

Repeat Step ❻ several times, moving the ping-pong ball in different orbits Note whether shadows are or are not cast.

Draw several of the "orbits" you test and note whether or not the ping-pong ball casts a shadow on the basketball or the basketball casts a shadow on the ping-pong ball (see the example below). You will need to spend some time "playing" with the ping-pong ball to find the positions where shadows occur.

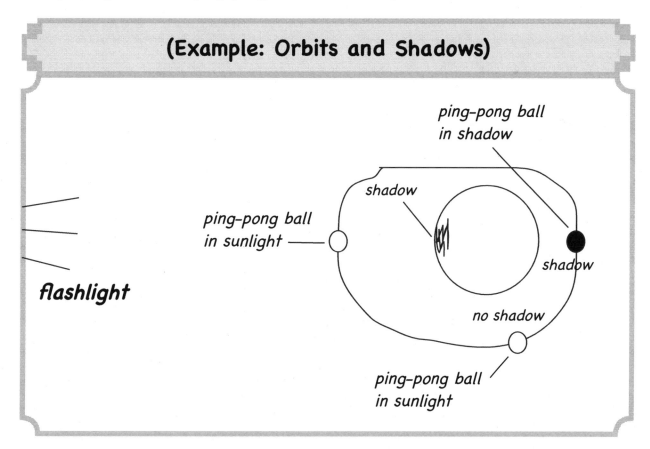

(Example: Orbits and Shadows)

ping-pong ball in shadow

shadow

ping-pong ball in sunlight

flashlight

shadow

no shadow

ping-pong ball in sunlight

ASTRONOMY

Orbits and Shadows

ASTRONOMY

More Orbits and Shadows

III. Conclusion

Based on your observations, discuss how a lunar eclipse occurs.

_____

_____

_____

_____

_____

_____

_____

_____

Based on your observations, explain how a solar eclipse occurs.

_____

_____

_____

_____

_____

_____

_____

_____

_____

ASTRONOMY

IV. Why?

An eclipse is a fascinating event to witness. When the Earth passes in between the Sun and the Moon, a lunar eclipse occurs, and when the Moon passes between the Sun and Earth, we get a solar eclipse. Both types of eclipses can give us valuable information about the Earth, Moon, and Sun.

In order for an eclipse to occur, the Sun, Earth, and Moon have to be precisely lined up. If they are not, there won't be an eclipse, or the eclipse will be partial. In a partial lunar eclipse, the shadow of Earth moves over only a part of the Moon. In a partial solar eclipse, only part of the Sun will be covered as the Moon passes in front of it.

Because the Moon's orbit around the Earth is a little bit tipped when compared to Earth's orbit around the Sun, the Moon, Earth, and Sun don't always line up precisely enough to create an eclipse. This is why there isn't a total eclipse of the Sun and a total eclipse of the Moon each time the Moon orbits the Earth. The Earth, Moon, and Sun aren't always lined up precisely enough.

Lunar eclipses occur only when the Moon is full, which is when it is at its farthest distance from the Sun and is passing directly behind the Earth. The Moon is the right size and the right distance from Earth for the Earth's shadow to completely cover the Moon during a total lunar eclipse.

It so happens that the Moon is at just the right distance from Earth that it can fully block out the disk of the Sun during a total solar eclipse. Solar eclipses occur only during a new moon phase when the Moon is lined up precisely between the Sun and the Earth. Even though the disk of the Sun is covered by the Moon during a solar eclipse, intense sunlight shines around the edges of the Moon. If a total or partial solar eclipse is viewed directly, the intense sunlight can cause permanent damage to the eyes.

An interesting fact about the Moon is that the same side of the Moon always faces Earth. When we see a full Moon, the Moon is positioned so that the side facing Earth is illuminated, and during the new (or dark) Moon, this side is not illuminated. Because it takes the Moon about four weeks to orbit Earth, this means that at any particular place on the Moon, daylight lasts for two weeks and nighttime lasts for two weeks.

ASTRONOMY

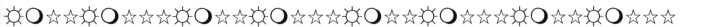

V. Just For Fun

Part A: Use your experimental setup to model how day and night occur on the Moon. Put a mark on the ping-pong ball to identify the side of the Moon that always faces Earth and then model the Moon's orbit.

Record your results.

Night and Day on the Moon

Part B: Think about how suns, planets, and moons might be arranged in different solar systems that we haven't yet visited. What do you think would happen with eclipses if you discovered a planet that, like Earth, had one moon, but the planet was orbiting two suns? What if a planet had two moons? What if the Sun were shining on the planet from above? What if Earth's Moon was a different shape, like a square or a dumbbell? What other different conditions can you think of? Model or draw some of your ideas and record your results in the following boxes.

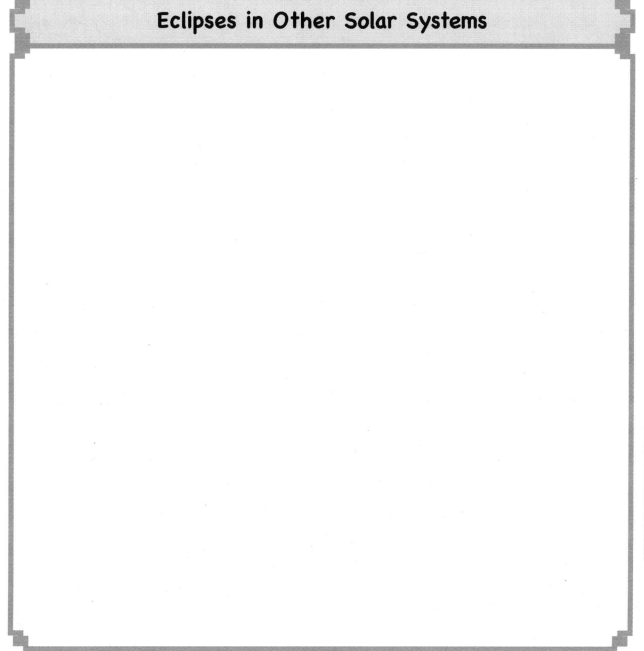

Eclipses in Other Solar Systems

More Eclipses in Other Solar Systems

ASTRONOMY

Experiment 20

Modeling the Moon

Introduction

Learn more about the Moon's features by building a model.

I. Think About It

❶ What do you think you can tell about the Moon's surface by looking at a photograph?

_____

_____

_____

_____

❷ What similarities do you think there are between Earth and the Moon?

_____

_____

_____

_____

❸ What differences do you think there are between Earth and the Moon?

_____

_____

_____

_____

ASTRONOMY

❹ Do you think it is possible for people to live on the Moon? Why or why not?

_____

_____

_____

_____

_____

❺ Do you think the first astronauts to walk on the Moon found anything surprising or things they did not already know? Why or why not?

_____

_____

_____

_____

_____

❻ Do you think what scientists have learned about the Moon could help with planning for travel to other planets? Why or why not?

_____

_____

_____

_____

_____

II. Experiment 20: Modeling the Moon   Date _____

Objective _____

_____

Hypothesis _____

_____

_____

Materials

modeling clay in the following colors:
    gray
    white
    brown
    red
butter knife or sculptor's knife
ruler

EXPERIMENT

Model building is an important part of science. Models help scientists visualize how something might look in three dimensions.

❶ Observe the cutaway image and the photographs of the Moon in the *Student Textbook*.

❷ Using modeling clay, build a model Moon that resembles the cutaway image in the *Student Textbook*. Include the core, mantle, and crust and note the colors used for them. Observe any color variations on the Moon's surface. As much as possible, duplicate the cutaway image and photographs with your model.

❸ Use a ruler to measure the diameter of your completed model Moon.

ASTRONOMY

Results

The real Moon is 3476.2 kilometers (2160 miles) in diameter. Compare the diameter of your model with the actual diameter of the Moon. Do the following steps to calculate how many times smaller your model is compared to the actual size of the Moon.

❶ Write the diameter of your model Moon in centimeters _____ or in inches _____. The diameter of the actual Moon is 3476.2 kilometers (2160 miles).

❷ Convert the diameter of your model Moon to kilometers.

(If you are using inches, first multiply by 2.54 to get centimeters.

_____ inches X 2.54 = _____ centimeters.)

Multiply the number of centimeters by 0.00001 to get kilometers. This will be a very small number.

_____ centimeters X 0.00001 = _____ kilometers.

❸ Divide the actual diameter of the Moon by the diameter of your model Moon.

3476.2 kilometers (actual Moon) ÷ _____ kilometers (model Moon) = _____.

This should be a very large number. It tells you how many times larger the real Moon is compared to your model Moon.

ASTRONOMY

III. Conclusion

How easy or difficult was it to build a model of the Moon?

_____

_____

_____

_____

_____

_____

_____

Based on your calculation, how much larger is the actual Moon compared
to your model Moon? What does this mean to you?

_____

_____

_____

_____

_____

_____

_____

_____

ASTRONOMY

IV. Why?

What does the surface of the Moon look like and what is inside the Moon? Building a model is a great way to learn more about the Moon. To build a model, you need to look carefully at the features of the Moon that you can observe, and you also need to consider what scientists think about the structure of the interior part you can't see.

Suppose you wanted to add more detail to your model Moon than you can see in the photograph in your textbook. You might try using your eyes to look at the Moon on a clear night. You can see that it has different features that form dark and light areas, but you can't see the details. To see more detail you could look through binoculars. By looking through a telescope you'd be able to see much more. For an even closer look, you could view different photographs taken from satellites and other spacecraft and also photos and videos taken by astronauts who walked on the Moon. By studying photographs of the Moon, you might observe that it has lots of craters of all different sizes and does not appear to have vegetation or running water. The facts and details you gathered through observation could be added to your model.

Model building can help you compare what you've discovered about the Moon to what you know about Earth. In what ways are they similar and how are they different? You know that both the Earth and the Moon are celestial bodies and the Earth orbits the Sun. Because the Moon orbits Earth, the Moon travels along with Earth around the Sun. Both Earth and the Moon are spheres, are made of rock, have layers inside, and have rocky crusts that are not smooth. Because the Moon is smaller than Earth, it has less gravity. If you watch videos of the Apollo astronauts, you can see them bouncing as they walk on the Moon because the gravity is so much weaker than that of Earth.

The Moon has almost no atmosphere. Earth has a dense atmosphere that supports life. The Moon has ice but doesn't have surface water. Without an atmosphere and liquid water, the Moon can't support life as Earth does. Some astrobiologists think there's a possibility that microorganisms might exist on the Moon because bacteria and archaea that live in very extreme environments have been found on Earth and similar organisms may be able to survive on celestial bodies like the Moon.

ASTRONOMY

V. Just For Fun

Imagine you are the designer of a permanent station on the Moon. What would the people need to live comfortably? What would they need for doing research? What would they do for fun? What else would they need? Write your ideas below, and on the next page draw a picture of your Moon station.

Ideas for a Moon Station

Station on the Moon

Experiment 21

Modeling the Planets

Introduction

Model the eight planets of our solar system to learn more about their similarities and differences.

I. Think About It

❶ If you were to make a list of some of Earth's features, what would they be?

_____

_____

_____

_____

_____

❷ Do you think anything can be learned by comparing the planets in our solar system? Why or why not?

_____

_____

_____

_____

_____

❸ Do you think all the Jovian planets are the same? Why or why not?

_____

_____

_____

_____

ASTRONOMY

❹ Do you think a planet's position from the Sun determines any of the planet's features? Why or why not?

_____

_____

_____

_____

_____

❺ What methods and technologies do you think scientists use to find out more about the planets?

_____

_____

_____

_____

_____

❻ Do you think when people go to Mars they will find anything surprising? Why or why not?

_____

_____

_____

_____

_____

ASTRONOMY

II. Experiment 21: Modeling the Planets   Date _____

Objective _____

_____

Hypothesis _____

_____

_____

Materials

    Modeling clay in the following colors:
        gray
        white
        brown
        red
        blue
        green
        orange
    butter knife or sculptor's knife
    colored pencils

EXPERIMENT

❶ Look closely at the images of the eight planets in your *Student Textbook*. Observe their relative sizes (which planets are larger or smaller than the others) and their shape and colors.

❷ In the following spaces write notes about what you observe from the textbook images of each planet. Using colored pencils, make a quick sketch of each planet, noting any important features, such as rings or spots, and the colors of the features. These notes will be used as a guide for building your models. Online references can be used to find more images of the planets. You can go to a website such as www.nasa.gov/ or do a search for individual planet images.

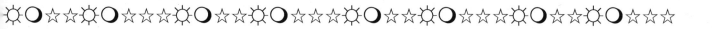

Mercury

_____

_____

_____

_____

Venus

_____

_____

_____

_____

Earth

_____

_____

_____

_____

Mars

_____

_____

_____

Jupiter

_____

_____

_____

_____

Saturn

_____

_____

_____

_____

Uranus

_____

_____

_____

_____

Neptune

_____

_____

_____

_____

ASTRONOMY

❸ Using modeling clay, create a model of each planet. Refer to your notes and sketches while building the models, and make sure that you keep the relative sizes in proportion (Jupiter is larger than Earth, Mercury is smaller than Venus, and so on).

Results

Observe the model planets you have created. Are they the correct relative size? Do they match the images in the book? Are they all spherical in shape? Record your observations below:

_____

_____

_____

_____

_____

_____

_____

_____

_____

_____

_____

_____

_____

III. Conclusion

How easy or difficult was it to build the models of the planets?

_____

_____

_____

_____

_____

_____

_____

Discuss how well your models do or do not represent the real planets.

_____

_____

_____

_____

_____

_____

_____

IV. Why?

Model building can help you compare the planets in our solar system to each other, observing how they are similar and how they are different. To build models, you need to do research to find out details about each planet. By doing research you will find information you can use to build your models as accurately as possible. You will also find much additional information that you won't use in your models but that will help you understand much more about the planets.

Knowing that Mercury, Venus, Earth, and Mars are made of rock and have rocky crusts that are not smooth will help you build models of them. Knowing that Jupiter, Saturn, Uranus, and Neptune are made of gases can help with building those models. Finding out that the planets are spherical in shape, the size of each planet, which have rings, and what their surfaces look like will help you build more accurate models.

By doing research you can also discover many other facts about the planets that you won't include in your models. You can find out that the Earth and the other planets in our solar system each has its own orbit around the Sun and the distance of each from the Sun is known. You can find out what the atmosphere of each planet is made of and how thick it is, whether or not the planet has liquid water, and the temperature of the planet. You can learn how long the days and years are on a particular planet and how much its axis is tipped. These are just a few of the things you can discover.

We know that Earth has a thick atmosphere, liquid water, and is the right distance from the Sun to support life. By comparing what is known about Earth and the other planets, you can begin to develop ideas, or theories, about whether life might exist on another planet, whether we might someday travel to it, and whether we might eventually be able to set up a base on the planet where people could live and do research.

Doing research to find out what has already been discovered is a fun part of science because it can lead to finding information that is unexpected and even amazing! And doing this kind of research gives scientists the background information they need in order to be able to come up with new ideas for new discoveries.

ASTRONOMY

V. Just For Fun

Imagine you are an astronomer using a powerful space telescope. You have just discovered a new planet, and the telescope brings detailed images to you. In the following box, name this new planet and list its features, such as what the planet is made of, what colors and patterns you can see, and whether it has water and life. Make a colored sketch of the planet and its features. If you'd like to see it in 3D, build a model of your new planet.

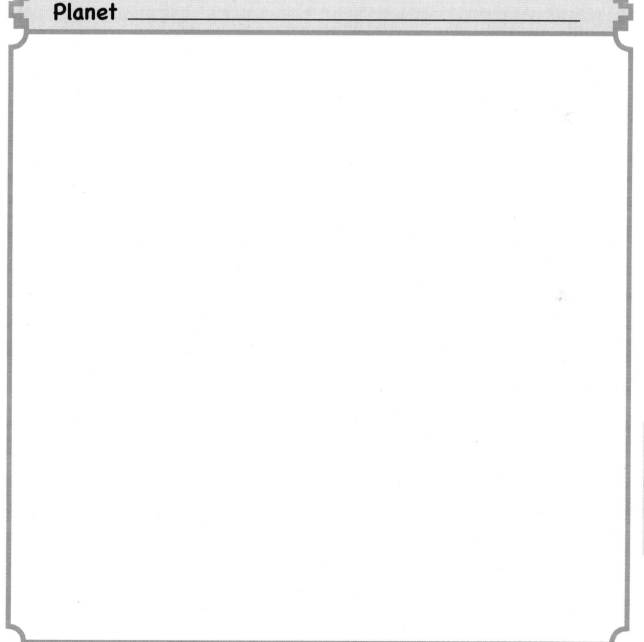

Planet _____

Experiment 22

Cameras Rolling!

Introduction

Create your own science movie!

I. Think About It

❶ Do you think science makes a good subject for movies? Why or why not?

_____

_____

_____

_____

❷ Think of a movie or TV program you watched that had a science or science fiction theme. Do you think the scientists were portrayed realistically? Why or why not?

_____

_____

_____

_____

❸ Do you think the science in the movie was portrayed in a way that was believable and/or possible? Why or why not?

_____

_____

_____

_____

❹ Do you think movies are better when the science and scientists in them are more realistic? Why or why not?

_____

_____

_____

_____

❺ What difficulties do you think filmmakers might encounter when including science and scientists in their films?

_____

_____

_____

_____

❻ Do you think movies about science can help the people making and viewing them learn more about science? Why or why not?

_____

_____

_____

_____

II. Experiment 22: Cameras Rolling!   Date _____

Objective _____

_____

Hypothesis _____

_____

_____

Materials

device that can record video

EXPERIMENT

In this experiment, you will make a video about science.

❶ Review Chapter 22 of the *Student Textbook* and find an area of science that you would like to explore in a movie that is based on science facts and discoveries.

❷ Decide what your movie will be about and what type of movie it will be. Will it be a factual documentary? Will it be a historical movie about a scientist or scientific discovery? Will it be instructional (how-to)? Will it be a drama based on real science? Will it be science fiction? Will it be something else?

❸ Write an outline for your story including the characters who will be in your movie.

❹ Write out a script of what your characters will say. Include notes about what you want them to be doing.

❺ Recruit friends and family to star in your movie.

❻ Film your movie.

Results

Show your movie to friends and family.

III. Conclusions

From your observations, what conclusions can you draw about making a scientific movie?

_____

_____

_____

_____

_____

_____

_____

_____

_____

_____

_____

_____

_____

_____

_____

IV. Why?

Making a movie can be a great way to learn more about science. It takes a lot of thought to determine the type of movie to be made and the subject area to be covered. In longer movies that involve science, a lot of research must be done to be able to portray science and scientists with accuracy. Writing and filming a scientific movie can be a very lengthy process.

Movie makers need to ask lots of questions as they are planning and producing a film. What events are important to the story and what will hold the audience's interest? What characters should be included in the telling of the story? How will it be told? How can science be depicted accurately? How can the characters be presented in a meaningful way? Where will it be filmed? What props are needed? Could it be filmed in a real laboratory or does a set need to be built?

Writers for movies involving science need to know how scientists think, how they perform research, and how scientific discoveries are put into use in the world. For historical movies, research must be done to learn about the different events that occurred, and then the most important events for telling the story have to be selected. For biographies of particular scientists, facts need to be learned about their lives and their discoveries. This may involve interviewing people.

Some movies are made by scientists themselves. Nature films are a good example. Biologists who are out in the field studying a particular living thing can present their research and conclusions, drawing from their notes and showing video that they or accompanying videographers have taken. There may be a writer involved who will come up with the narrative, and many other people will most likely be involved in other aspects of making the movie.

In science fiction films, depicting science accurately will make them much more believable. In the best films, writers start with today's technology and imagine how it will have advanced in the future.

V. Just For Fun

Watch a movie or TV show that is based on science. Evaluate whether you think science and scientists are portrayed realistically. What could you change that would make the movie better or portray science more realistically? Did the storyline hold your interest? What else did you observe about science in the movie?

Record your observations on the next page.

- Or -

Evaluate the film you made. What things about it could you change to make it more accurate? What things would you change to make it more interesting? Do you think it would be fun and helpful to get more people involved in planning and creating the movie?

How many other ideas can you think of for making more movies about science, and what type of movie would each be? How many different science subjects could you include? On the next page list your ideas.

Optional: Choose one idea and make a new movie.

Science Movie Notes

More REAL SCIENCE-4-KIDS Books
by Rebecca W. Keller, PhD

Building Blocks Series yearlong study program—each Student Textbook has accompanying Laboratory Notebook, Teacher's Manual, Lesson Plan, Study Notebook, Quizzes, and Graphics Package

Exploring Science Book K (Activity Book)
Exploring Science Book 1
Exploring Science Book 2
Exploring Science Book 3
Exploring Science Book 4
Exploring Science Book 5
Exploring Science Book 6
Exploring Science Book 7
Exploring Science Book 8

Focus On Series unit study program—each title has a Student Textbook with accompanying Laboratory Notebook, Teacher's Manual, Lesson Plan, Study Notebook, Quizzes, and Graphics Package

Focus On Elementary Chemistry
Focus On Elementary Biology
Focus On Elementary Physics
Focus On Elementary Geology
Focus On Elementary Astronomy

Focus On Middle School Chemistry
Focus On Middle School Biology
Focus On Middle School Physics
Focus On Middle School Geology
Focus On Middle School Astronomy

Focus On High School Chemistry

Super Simple Science Experiments

21 Super Simple Chemistry Experiments
21 Super Simple Biology Experiments
21 Super Simple Physics Experiments
21 Super Simple Geology Experiments
21 Super Simple Astronomy Experiments
101 Super Simple Science Experiments

Note: A few titles may still be in production.

Gravitas Publications Inc.
www.gravitaspublications.com
www.realscience4kids.com